מסורה

ArtScroll Series®

Rabbi Nosson Scherman / Rabbi Meir Zlotowitz

General Editors

Our Wondrous

Published by

Mesorah Publications, ltd

World

Wonders hidden
below the surface

by

Rabbi Avrohom Katz

FIRST EDITION
First Impression … October 1999

Published and Distributed by
MESORAH PUBLICATIONS, LTD.
4401 Second Avenue / Brooklyn, N.Y 11232

Distributed in Europe by
J. LEHMANN HEBREW BOOKSELLERS
20 Cambridge Terrace
Gateshead, Tyne and Wear
England NE8 1RP

Distributed in Israel by
SIFRIATI / A. GITLER
10 Hashomer Street
Bnei Brak 51361

Distributed in Australia and New Zealand by
GOLDS BOOK & GIFT SHOP
36 William Street
Balaclava 3183, Vic., Australia

Distributed in South Africa by
KOLLEL BOOKSHOP
Shop 8A Norwood Hypermarket
Norwood 2196, Johannesburg, South Africa

Typography by CompuScribe at ArtScroll Studios, Ltd.

Printed in the United States of America by Noble Book Press Corp.
Bound by Sefercraft, Quality Bookbinders, Ltd., Brooklyn N.Y. 11232

RABBI B. RAKOW
RAV OF GATESHEAD
138 WHITEHALL ROAD,
GATESHEAD NE8 1TP
Tyne & Wear
TEL. 0632-773012

בצלאל בהרה"ג ר' יום טוב ליפמאן ראקאוו

אב"ד דנייטסהעד

ב"ה _____ יום _____

הנה יב"ג הרי שלוחכם אליה הבן קלף פ"ש ...
... ס ... פי ... ס ...
ולהעריה ... הכבר ... האזרח ...
... האמר קל ... ירמ רק ...
... המקויים ... ...
... קיימ ... החלקות ...
... כן ... ...
... ...

כ... סים ... ...
ואחת ... ...
...

... פ"י ...
... ...

יה רן שאן

... האריאל ...
הק' בצלאל ראקאוו

הסכמה מאת
הרב ר׳ מתתי׳ סלומון, שליט״א
משגיח רוחני דישיבת בית מדרש גבוה דלייקווד

It is with very special joy that I write these few lines of appreciation on the unique work of a very beloved *talmid* whose friendship I have cherished for over 25 years.

ירא שמים, בן תורה and בעל is renowned as a הר״ר אברהם טוביה הכהן כ״ץ שליט״א מדות. But most outstanding is his אמונה — which is what this book is all about.

The chapters of this book do not just contain clever comparisons in parable form, but they are דברים היוצאים מן הלב — sincere words emanating from a pure heart, designed to enter the heart and strengthen the reader's awareness of הקב״ה in all his surroundings.

This ספר is an updated שער הבחינה, expanding on the theme begun by the בעל חובות הלבבות, and continued through the years up till our times by such גדולים as the חזון איש in his קונטרס אמונה בטחון and the Steipler זצ״ל in his ספר חיי עולם.

The author of this work has his own original approach, and although his style is sometimes light, one is never diverted from the central theme of the book which is to make the reader — at the end of each chapter — gasp in astonishment and exclaim over and over again — נפלאות הבורא! נפלאות הבורא!

זכה המחבר שליט״א להיות ממזכי הרבים הגדולים בדורנו על ידי שעוריו המתוקים בכמה מוסדות בעירנו וכמה מקומות במדינתנו - ועכשיו זיכהו השי״ת להרחיב גבולו על ידי ספר נפלא זה שיגיע בעזה״י לכל קצווי תבל ותרבה הדעת והאמונה בעולם - אשרי חלקו!

ויהי רצון שיפוצו מעיינותיו חוצה ויראה ברכה בעמלו כל הימים.

ממני הכו״ח באה״ר

מתתי׳ חײם סלומון

מתתיהו חיים סלומון

בֵּית מִדְרָשׁ לְמוֹרוֹת

JEWISH TEACHERS' TRAINING COLLEGE

Founded by: Mr A. KOHN

FOR TEACHERS IN DAY SCHOOLS, HEBREW CLASSES AND NURSERY - SCHOOLS

Principal: Rabbi M. MILLER

**50, BEWICK ROAD
GATESHEAD NE8 4DQ**
Telephone: 091-477 2620
091-477 1566

ב"ה

It gives me considerable satisfaction to write a few words of approbation with regard to the book "Our Amazing World" compiled by Rabbi A. Katz who has been a most successful lecturer at the Gateshead Jewish Teachers' Training College for several years.

Rabbi Katz is endowed with an unusual gift both in the written and spoken word to demonstrate the incontrovertible wonders in the universe at large and in the personal human physique, thus accomplishing the dual function of שאו מרום עיניכם וראו מי ברא אלה — "Raise your eyes to the heavans and contemplate, 'Who created all this?'" (Yeshayah, 40:26) and מבשרי אחזה אלוק — "And from my own flesh I can perceive my Creator" (Job 19:26) in its positive sense.

Rabbi Katz's writings are infused with both wit and erudition and his style fascinates the reader. He has been a regular contributor to "Yated Ne'eman" and the present volume is a compilation of those articles.

The book is an invaluable source from which the reader will derive an appreciation of the wondrous world of the Creator and it will undoubtedly strengthen his Emunah. It is a path trodden by אברהם אבינו and commended to us by so many of our גדולים; in particular, חובות הלבבות, רמב"ם and חזון איש.

In seeking to emulate their illustrious example, albeit in a modern context and idiom, Rabbi Katz has provided the reader with a wealth of material from which he can attain greater awareness of the גדלות הבורא.

I profoundly hope that "Our Amazing World" will reach the minds and hearts of a wide public to accomplish the purpose for which it was written.

Rabbi M. Miller
Principal, Gateshead J T T C

Table of Contents

Foreword

Chances are that you are reading this indoors. If so, take a look at the window. Most windows are made of transparent glass. Do you have any idea when the first glass window was invented? On your wrist there is likely to be a wristwatch. When did people first begin wearing wristwatches? Given the prevalent view that real progress was introduced to the world shortly before we were born, it would not be difficult to convince people that glass windows were a product of the Industrial Revolution, and that wristwatches became popular in the mid-20th century. It is for this reason that books that catalogue the history of inventions are so revealing.

Apart from informing us that glazed windows started to appear around the time of Rabbi Akiva (1st century C.E.), and that the earliest wristwatches were being manufactured in Geneva in 1790, they perform another vital service. In fascinating detail they reveal how throughout history, there have been people with active (and inventive) minds who were able to apply their intelligence to contemporary situations, and with their ingenious inventions, enrich or simplify the lives of their fellow citizens.

On any given day, the mechanism of the alarm clock that wakes us, the plastic of the *negel vasser* cup, the plastic of the toothbrush (handle and bristles), the zipper that fastens clothes so simply, the electricity that heats the water for the morning coffee (not to mention the instant coffee), frozen food for dinner, margarine on the bread, spectacles with which to view the world clearly, the car or train that transports us so efficiently, the ballpoint pen to write with, the fax to delight, the telephone that has added new vistas to the human voice, paper clips to hold loose ends together, detergents, aerosols, jet engines — from the deceivingly simple safety pin to the icon of the modern world, the computer — we benefit from the intelligence and applied wisdom of thousands of our predecessors.

Applying our minds to the world around us is not the exclusive precinct of would-be inventors. It is the most Jewish of occupations. The first direct request of the *Amidah* is the plea for intellect. Indeed, man's claim to superiority over animals hinges on the faculty of intellect. The Talmud (*Nedarim* 41a) quotes Abaye who emphasized that intellect is man's most treasured possession. "He who has intellect has everything." Potentially at least, every man has intellect. The question is whether he wishes to use it.

To the Jew, it is not so much a choice but an imperative. We are commanded to study the Torah, delve, inquire, research, acquire its knowledge, and then teach it to others. The highest accolade that can be received is the title *"talmid chacham"* — a wise pupil. Intellect and Torah study are synonymous. In addition, the Torah commands us to believe in G-d. Indeed, that command is the basis upon which every aspect of Judaism rests.

Emunah — belief in G-d — is a multi-stranded entity; and there are several ways in which a person can acquire a firm belief. The more one studies Torah, the stronger the conviction that the vast, infinite interconnected edifice that Torah comprises is the work of an Infinite intelligence. A close study of the history of the Jewish people (that most endangered of species) and its remarkable survival throughout the millennia, its triumphs and adversities, its disproportionate prominence in world events, its cyclical occupation and expulsion from the Land of Israel, all unswervingly plotted by age-old prophecies accurate to the smallest detail, point a definitive finger at a Supreme Controller of world events.

High on the list of methods with which one can acquire *emunah* is one that requires nothing more than an honest mind. It is an approach that can be used by anyone at any time. Imagine that you are walking along the road, with houses on both sides. Take a look at one of the houses. How many individual component parts do you think comprise the whole edifice? How many single bricks, screws, nails, pipes, joints, electrical wire, slates, panes of glass (assuming that the house was built after 100 C.E.) frames, and planks of wood does the house possess? You know that each component part (not to mention the furnishings and individual possessions of the owner) has been manufactured and placed into position with wisdom, precision and careful planning. The larger the edifice, the more complex the planning.

Then think of yourself as you stride along the street. How many component parts make up the human body? You can begin with the millions upon millions of cells that help the body to grow and maintain itself, each one of which is more complicated than the city in which you live. Then continue with blood circulation, the body's very own integrated transport system (which, laid end to end stretches tens of thousands of miles) that delivers vital nutrients to every single cell in the human body. Think of the vast, complex maze of nerves that makes up the human brain. Bear in mind the systems that enable the body to function, obtaining oxygen, digesting food and disposing of waste. Give a thought to the hormonal glands, the skeletal system, and to the protective skin, hair and nails. The apartment blocks that straddle the street are as complicated as a doll's house in comparison to the limitless wizardry of a human being. We know that an architect planned the house. The sign outside a new construction site reveals his identity. Who made man? An honest mind will happily admit that all of Creation is the work of a Supreme Creator. This was the thought process that led Abraham our forefather to discover the Creator, and by so doing, inspire a legacy that is as relevant today as it was three and a half thousand years ago.

It is interesting to note that the human body (and all aspects of Creation for that matter) is so well constructed that it can never be equaled by imitation. Robots have never successfully copied the body's ability to walk in a well-balanced way on two legs, let alone its huge variety of fast-action, precise movements and its range of sight, hearing, touch and other senses. Even the most advanced computers do not come close to the human brain's capacity for intelligent thought, learning and creativity.

It is true that there is a body of opinion that denies a planned and intelligent Creation, preferring to place their trust in a postulated theory of chance. The fact that the name of the theory — "Evolution" — so closely resembles the words "evil-lushon," which to the Jewish ear indicate forbidden speech, is surely no accident. There can be no greater example of evil speech, or a pernicious theory, than one that seeks to deny the Creator. Nor can there be a more dishonest one. Sufficient numbers of scientists have coherently and devastatingly rebutted Darwin's theory of evolution to convince an honest mind that Darwinism today functions more as an anachronistic ideology than as a modern scientific theory.

This book has been written to help honest minds direct their intellect towards discovering G-d. In the various chapters, the readers will find that the conventional approach to discovering the "Wonders of Creation" — namely, going for an outing to the countryside, looking at the fields and mountains, filling one's lungs with fresh air, stretching one's arms out and declaring *"Ah, Niflaos Haborei!"* — has not been used. If intellect is the key to discovering G-d within the created world, then you can save yourself the expense of traveling anywhere. Just look at your hand. Ponder the complexity of sight, the incomparable dexterity of fingers, and belief in a Creator is literally at your fingertips.

Twice daily a Jew is enjoined to love God with all his heart. If the heart is the idiomatic equivalent of the mind, then the chapters that follow will give ample opportunity for the honest mind to discover, and then love, its Creator. No task could be more important, and none more rewarding.

Acknowledgments

The purpose of this book is to teach how to recognize the Creator and be grateful for His endless kindness. There can be no better training for this vital exercise than to recognize the favors that one receives from family, friends and Society. I consider it a great merit to have been able to learn, settle down and bring up a family in Gateshead – the famous Torah town of England.

This book would not have seen the light of day had it not been for the constant encouragement, cajoling and gentle arm-twisting of my good friend, R' Dovid Morgan. His contribution to the finished product is enormous and I am greatly indebted to him for his friendship, support and encouragement in the publication of this book, as well as his close involvement in various educational projects. May *Hashem Yisbarach* bless him, together with his family, with the good health and vigor to continue his vital work for many years to come *ad meah ve'esrim shanah*.

Moshe Aharon Ruskin provided the photography, and his artistic talent has contributed greatly to the finished product.

All the chapters contained in the book have appeared in the weekly *Yated Ne'eman* as articles under the pen-name Tuvia Cohen. I am extremely grateful to the worthy editors for their permission to reprint the articles in book form.

Mesorah Publications, popularly known as Artscroll, is a publishing company whose staff combines professionalism with pleasantness. It has been both a privilege and a pleasure to make their acquaintance, and particular thanks are due to Rabbi Nosson Sherman, the General Editor; Rabbi Avrohom Biderman, who master-minded the production; Mrs. Judy Dick, whose skillful editing made the original Queen's English comprehensible to those on both sides of the Atlantic; and Mrs. Rivkah Hamaoui who compiled the index. In addition, Mrs. Faygie Weinbaum and Mrs. Mindy Stern are to be commended for their superb proofreading.

My dear family has no desire to be mentioned. But they deserve it, for being so loyal, encouraging and helpful. Each one is wonderful, and each one should be blessed with everything that is good.

The greatest thanks of all goes to *Hashem Yisbarach*, for granting me the privilege of having been able to discover and relate a minute amount of endless wisdom, in this — His — World of Wisdom. May it be His will that I be able to continue this work in good health, and together with all our People merit seeing the great day when all inhabitants of the world will gladly acknowledge the true Master of the Universe, the source of all wisdom.

The Old Master

They say that money is a word that speaks all languages. So does the word lottery. Nearly every country has one, and with minor variations, the principle is the same. For a small monetary outlay, you buy the opportunity to win a vast sum of money. Even England, that last bastion of traditionalism, has fallen victim to the lure of instant wealth. Even though the chance of winning the first prize is remote (in England it is one in 14 million), the purchase of a ticket is a license to dream. And dream they do. "Just think ... if I won ... 40 million ...pounds/dollars/shekels/pengö/lire ..." Let me ask you a practical question. Let's say that you were the lucky (or unlucky, depending on whether you think that riches can buy happiness, but that is another question ...) winner of a vast sum. What could you spend it on? After you had paid your phone bill and the butcher, decorated the front of your house and sponsored a grand *kiddush*, how would you spend the millions? What single item can you buy that costs the millions that you now have to spend? The answer is simple. An Old Master.

There is a painting that hangs in the Louvre, in Paris. It is a portrait of a woman, painted by Leonardo da Vinci, called *The Mona Lisa*. It hangs behind a bulletproof glass screen (some years ago a man who obviously did not appreciate a good painting threw a bottle of ink at the poor lady!) and although in real terms it is nothing spectacular, it is doubtful whether five lotteries would buy you this painting. What is true of da Vinci is true of Van Gogh, Picasso or Rembrandt. These (and others like them) are master painters, and their Old Masters are the national treasures of many countries. These men were masters of their craft. Take Rembrandt. Living as he did in Amsterdam in the early 1600s, he was privileged to have as his neighbor Rabbi Menasseh ben Israel. Through his close association with the man who was responsible for the return of Jews to England, and also due to the prominence of the Jewish population in Amsterdam, many of Rembrandt's paintings have Biblical themes. However, the painting that made Rembrandt famous was far different in character. In 1631, Rembrandt, who then was new to Amsterdam, was asked by Dr. Nicholas Tulp to make the doctor's annual anatomy lesson the subject of a painting. Anatomy lessons were public events, and people paid to get into the theater where they were held. Tulp was famous, and told Rembrandt exactly how he wanted himself presented, but the young artist was left to decide how everything else was going to look. In the painting, the great anatomy expert has opened the dead subject's hand and arm, and is holding the flexor muscles with metal forceps. Rembrandt contrasts

Painted by the talented hand of Rembrandt, but who created the hand?

Dr. Tulp's strong and skillful hands with the bloodless muscle and cartilage of his victim. *The Anatomy Lesson of Dr. Tulp* made Rembrandt famous, and from that point on portrait commissions poured into his new studio.

The hand of the painter draws a hand, and the painting is valued at millions of dollars. How much would you pay for the hand itself? Not the lifeless, motionless, inanimate hand on canvas, but the real hand — the moving, agile, flexible, warm and living hand — how much is its value? Hold your hands out in front of your face, and look at them. How did you tie your shoelaces this morning? How did you turn the pages of your *siddur*? When you made yourself a scrambled egg, how did you pick up the egg without cracking it, then crack it on the side of a glass, lift the glass without allowing it to fall to the floor and smash into smithereens, and the hundreds of similar, very precise actions every day? Look at your hand. Engineers have tried for years to build machines that mimic the human hand. But none of these devices has come close to our range of movements. Robot machines on assembly lines carry out certain simple repetitive tasks in a tireless fashion. But a robot welder-arm cannot spray paint, and a robot suction-grab cannot tighten screws. Each device is designed to do only one of a few of the multiple tasks that our hands can do. For example: You are standing in front of a class. For some inexplicable reason, the students are not paying attention. It is incredible that your awesome personality does not mesmerize them into instant and respectful silence, but that's life. An undercurrent of chatter and nonattentiveness fills the room. How would you bring the class to attention, make the students aware of your impatience, without using your voice? Take your middle finger, and pass your thumb quickly over the surface of that long finger. This will produce a clicking sound, which, with practice, is both commanding and authoritative. That is your great hand, the most multivaried tool ever designed. Price — free of charge.

The human hand is perfectly designed for its many tasks. Similarly, every single creature in the animal kingdom possesses the hands that it requires. Let me ask you a question. Imagine that you had to change the light bulb. Could you do it? For sure, stand on a chair, and using your two hand-tools, you would carefully and skillfully exert pressure on the light bulb, achieving a perfect balance between the force sufficient to push the bulb into its socket, but insufficient to crack the bulb. A masterful performance, bearing in mind that your hands are powerful enough to smash through a plank of wood or change the shape of an enemy's nose. What would you do, though, if the ceiling was too high for you to reach the light by means of a chair? May I suggest that using your hands and feet, you walk up the wall and out along the ceiling, and by keeping a grip with your feet on the smooth surface of the ceiling, change the bulb? You can try it, but you are more likely to achieve some bumps on the head than changes of light. Your hands have not been designed for walking up walls. Would you like to meet some hands that have?

May we introduce you to the gecko. A gecko is a lizard with a long tail and four legs. Geckos move fast, and have the amazing ability to run up smooth walls and across ceilings in pursuit of a fly to eat. Very often they are to be found hanging upside down. Many of them live in houses (don't look now, they may be watching!) where there are plenty of cracks and crevices in which to rest or hide. Insects attracted by the lights, particularly at night, provide a plentiful supply of food. The big question is: How do they manage to walk up walls and across very flat ceilings? How do they walk up vertical sheets of glass? How do they defy the laws of gravity? The answer is that they have been provided with special pads on their feet. These pads are covered with millions of tiny hooks, like bristles on a brush, each ending in a suction pad. These grip even the smoothest surfaces, providing traction, and the toes can support several times the gecko's own weight. A fantastic tool such as the gecko's feet cannot be developed. No amount of running up a wall will enable you to grow suction pads (even though many people complain of being driven up the wall, they rarely are), and without suction pads, how would you run up walls? The gecko has had its specialized feet since its creation, and since that time they have them still, and no creature in the world has since developed them.

Claws are another fierce addition which have been granted to the animals that need them. No one would like to meet the razor-sharp claws of a lion or tiger, the cutting power of which is too frightening to contemplate, but you might like to know that when it walks along it makes not a sound, for those swordlike claws are retractable. If you ever let your nails grow long, try retracting them when they get in the way! The lions manage. The more homely squirrel has special equipment for climbing in both directions. Its ankle can be twisted around to point backwards — behind the animal — so that the claws on the hind feet can act as anchors for the descent as well as the ascent. Try twisting your ankle — on second thought, do not try to twist your ankle — and see how you fare. Neither hunting animals nor climbing trees are part of our routine, so we are equipped with neither capability. We, like all of the Creator's creatures, have what we require.

And we do require a thumb. The thumb is a virtual virtuoso. It moves in a different plane to the other four fingers, and because it can move to touch them all, is invaluable in providing grip. It performs about 45 percent of the hand's work. You could manage reasonably well without one of the other four digits, but a hand without a thumb is like a pair of pliers with one jaw missing. If you want to be convinced of the great gift of a thumb, try to fasten your top shirt button with only your four fingers, or sew a button onto your shirt (threading the needle first!). Then try to tie your shoelace. The whole hand is a remarkably sophisticated and indispensable piece of machinery. In the dark, the hands substitute for eyes. The sense of touch is so keen that you don't have to look at the coins in your pocket to find the coin of your choice. Your fingers can find one for you. If you were a farmer, you could run soil through your fingers and determine its properties; if you were a tailor, you could judge by feel the quality of a fabric. These are extraordinary achievements! As tough as a hammer, as sensitive as a feather, the hands lend expression, convey warmth, and link us to the world in a myriad of ways. Pointing, pounding, pushing, or painting, no tool exists that is so flexible, or so valuable. Designed to perfection, each set uniquely imprinted, warm and strong, safe and expressive, adroit and skillful — how much would you pay for an Old Master painting of them? And how much should we pay our Master Designer, Hashem *Yisbarach*, for a real live warm pair of wonderful hands to carry us through life? Worth thinking about, isn't it?

Look After the Children

Teachers, beware! Every so often, schools organize meetings at which parents can discuss their children's progress. Teachers look forward to these meetings with some degree of eagerness, for it affords them the opportunity to speak directly to the parents and deliver a frank appraisal of the child's performance. The meeting has been called, and the teacher sits behind his desk, pretending to mark a pile of books, the epitome of efficiency and wisdom. The mother stalks into the room, with the reluctant father in tow. Smiling in anticipation, she asks, "So, how is my little

Moishele doing?" The teacher sees the family resemblance, and is suddenly aware that beaming in front of him is the mother of the biggest pest that humanity has ever produced. He feels like a spider whose victim has just walked into the web. The teacher then begins to give a vivid account of the activities of the class nuisance, with a detailed analysis of the character faults that her darling Moishele demonstrates. Carried away by his own eloquence, the teacher does not notice the change on the mother's face. The smile quickly fades and is replaced by a look of annoyance, then anger, then undiluted animosity! Teacher, beware! You have challenged her maternal instinct — an insult to her son is a personal attack on herself. It will take all of the father's powers of restraint to dissuade the mother from bending her umbrella around the teacher's head. "Speak about my Moishele like that — a *chutzpah!*"

A lady who takes a peek into a baby carriage, and coos to the doting mother, "Oh! He looks just like you!" gives enormous pleasure. If she adds, "Do you mind if I give him a banana?" she is likely to be sent into orbit! Meddle with maternal instinct at your peril.

There seems to be no limit on what parents will do for their young. It could be in the middle of the night, it could be that the mother is exhausted, and has already been up several times for her baby. But let Junior emit but a tiny whimper, while Dad snores on blissfully, Mommy will dutifully attend to the needs of her tiny infant. What is true of humans is also true in the world of animals. When little birds are hatched from their eggs, all they want is food, warmth, shelter, and more food. A pair of titmice (a type of bird) gave their brood food 10,685 times in 14 days. A female wren fed her young 1,217 times in 16 hours! The parental instinct in protecting their young is so powerful that parents will willingly endanger their own lives to protect their offspring. A rhinoceros is the world's second largest land animal and weighs two tons. It is equipped with a fearsome weapon — a large horn on its snout which can reach lengths of five feet. It is hard

Precious maternal instinct. Is it accidental?

enough to remain unbroken even in a charge against a solid object. The ponderous rhino is usually a docile animal, contentedly munching leaves, unless it has cause to believe that its young are endangered. The mother rhino tends her baby with unusual affection long after he is perfectly capable of fending for himself. With total disregard to consequences, she will charge any menace within sight. Pity the menace at the end of the five-foot spear!

There is no one as brave as a mother protecting her young. Ever heard the expression "as frightened as a mouse"? Not in the following case. An American biologist once heard squeaks of terror while studying deer on a ranch. He turned and saw a five-foot racer snake gliding up a low tree; in its mouth a tiny field mouse struggled vainly. Suddenly, the mother mouse ran up the tree and attacked the reptile. The second mouse bit into the snake's body several times, then got a firm grip and hung on grimly. The snake squirmed and feinted savagely, but could not bite the second mouse as long as the baby mouse remained in its mouth. The snake dropped its victim and turned to settle the score with the little tormentor who was biting into its back. The brave ruse worked. Instantly releasing its grip, the attacking mouse sprang to the ground and ran to safety with its rescued little one.

Motherly instinct might be vital for the protection of the young, but even that would be insufficient when the animals require specific mechanism for the birth and survival of their young. In case you imagine that fathers have no share in the wonders of survival, listen to this. Down in the Antarctic live the penguins. They spend most of their lives swimming in the icy Southern Ocean (kept warm by two layers of short, tightly packed feathers and by a layer of fat under their skin). They only leave the sea at breeding times, walking up to 100 miles, year after year, to the very rookeries (breeding places) where they themselves were hatched. Each female lays one egg, passes it to the male, and goes back to the sea to feed. For up to nine weeks, the male keeps the egg warm with a special flap of skin just above its feet. The feather-covered flap of skin fits over the egg like a tea cozy, allowing the egg to develop. During his nine-week wait, father penguin has no break whatsoever, and eats nothing. He survives from his own store of fat, and subsequently grows progressively thinner. Around the time the chick hatches, the female returns (how does she know precisely when to return, and to which location?) with a store of food. The tiny chick penguin reaches inside mommy's beak, whereupon mommy obligingly regurgitates the contents of her stomach. While the chick is growing, it keeps warm by standing on its parents' feet, and snuggles under the special flap. Handy things, warm flaps of skin — imagine having your own warm pockets, not in your coat, but on your body! Why not grow some? For the penguins it is no luxury, but a necessity to ensure the successful production of future penguins. Without the warm flap, there would be a frozen egg. It would be the end of the penguins. What it requires for its survival it receives from the Manufacturer.

Everyone knows that there are no flies in winter. Flies, like many animals, are cold-blooded animals (which means that they cannot regulate their body heat), so when the temperature drops, so do they. May we present you with a problem? Imagine (and for this you require a very vivid imagination!) that you are a cold-blooded animal that lays eggs. You have no way of elevating your own body temperature, but the eggs that you lay have to be kept at a constant warm level. How will you cope? Enter the python (and exit the reader!). Three to four months after mating, the female python lays up to 100 eggs. She gathers the eggs into a pile and coils her body around them for about three months until they hatch. By a special kind of shivering, the mother python can raise her body temperature by about 46 degrees (Farenheit) while she incubates the eggs. She only leaves her eggs for occasional visits to the water and for rare meals. There are two factors of interest here. Firstly the python is able to perform the impossible — to elevate her own temperature level with a "special" shivering. No one ever taught mother python how to perform her special shiver. But she knows exactly how it goes. Secondly, somehow, she knows that the eggs require a higher temperature than she can produce naturally. Who told her that? Inborn mechanisms do not come from nowhere. No one owns a car that, while parked outside his home overnight, "somehow" senses the temperature, and should it drop beneath zero, induces the windshield to perform a "special" shiver that generates heat and prevents frost from forming.

No one, except crocodiles, likes crocodiles. They suffer

from rather a negative public image, possibly due to the fact that they lurk unseen in the water with just their snout and cold eyes visible above the water, waiting, patiently, for their supper to come closer to the water's edge before lunging forward at lightning speed with their razor-sharp teeth ... But for all that, it is a most caring parent. Each year, the female Nile Crocodile (according to some, the plague of *tz'fardei'a* was not frogs, but crocodiles — not a pleasant thought!) lays up to 40 eggs in a nest, dug in the sand above the waterline on the riverbank. She builds the nest in a shady place, about 10 inches deep, so that the eggs keep at an even temperature — not varying more than 5°. She covers the eggs with sand, and both parents guard them during the 90-day incubation. When it is ready to hatch, the young crocodile makes loud piping calls from within its egg! The mother hears her unborn baby loud and clear, and scrapes away the sand covering the eggs. As the eggs hatch, she gently picks up each baby with those same razor-sharp teeth, and carries them in a special pouch at the bottom of her mouth to a "nursery" pool area off the river. The young crocodile stays in the nursery for about two months, guarded jealously by its parents. Everyone knows that the crocodile is not known for its kindness or compassion. Yet to its own children, it allows them to crawl in and out of its terrifying mouth, never knowingly biting or scratching them in the process. And where did the "special" pouch come from? Why don't we have one to store extra *cholent* on Shabbos dinner? Which came first, its babies or its pouch? One without the other has little purpose. Like everything in the designed world, it arrived as a personalized finished product.

What would you do if the only habitation you could find was on the ledge of a cliff? The perils of a cliffhanger are obvious, not least the danger of sleepwalking! You, an adult, can take care, but what will you do with your children? Especially if the children come in the shape of eggs, how will you prevent them rolling off the cliff! Quite a problem! Up in the Arctic, many birds lay their eggs on cliffs so that ene-mies on the ground cannot reach them. One particular species, the *guillemots*, lay their eggs on bare ledges. The eggs are specially designed to be pointed at one end, so that if they are knocked, they roll around in a circle instead of forward, off the ledge.

Specially shaped eggs do not happen by accident. Together with the myriad of essential features prevalent in parental care of their children, it is a classic illustration that the Designer of the world is desirous of the world continuing suc-cessfully — from generation to generation.

Just a Cup of Coffee

The flight across the Atlantic was most pleasant. Perhaps it was the tail wind, or the restful sleep that you were able to enjoy — the fact is that time really flew. The meal was superb — special kosher naturally — but what food! One doesn't like to go into details, but it isn't every day that you eat smoked salmon with salmon mousse, followed by chilled mango with citrus fruits, accompanied by vegetarian timbale of aubergines and hazelnuts, and then topped off with vanilla and mocha ice cream, all for your dinner. Take-off was smooth, landing imperceptible, the cabin crew impeccably polite.

"Thank you for choosing Luxury Airlines," said the recorded announcement just before you disembarked, "We do hope that we can be of service to you again." You hope so too!

Have you ever wondered why it is that airplane pilots behave differently than orchestra conductors? At the end of a virtuoso performance, during which the conductor waves his arms furiously, stabbing at an invisible enemy with his baton, the audience erupts into rapturous applause. In response, the conductor, with due modesty and humility, turns to the audience and bows, humbly accepting their resounding accolade. After he has been saturated by the praise, he stands and graciously waves an arm in the direction of the orchestra, indicating that they too have had a part in the musical triumph. All he has done was to coordinate various sounds and perhaps 20 musical instruments into a harmonious and pleasing recital of a composition which he himself did not even compose. Yet the listeners are ecstatic. In stark contrast, the airplane pilot has navigated a thin tube of metal at a speed exceeding 500 miles per hour across an inhospitable ocean at a height of some five miles. Four hundred passengers depend on the skill and expertise of the pilot for much more than their vanilla and mocha ice cream. And yet, throughout the performance, the pilot remains cocooned in his cabin, never seen by his passengers. Even at the end of the flight, he remains incognito — no one applauds, no one cheers and no one calls for an encore. If the cabin crew did not stand by the exit bidding everyone farewell, it is doubtful if anyone would even thank the people who successfully brought you to your destination safely. How come?

The answer is simple. In the case of the conductor, he has demonstrated a talent. Single-handed (sometimes with two hands!), he molds diverse sounds into one melodious whole. The achievement is incontrovertible, and recognized. The airplane, however is different. The pilot is not responsible for the plane. He did not design it, he did not acquire the components, nor did he assemble them. He did not drill the oil

How many millions of people are needed to produce one cup of coffee?

from the ground, refine it into aviation fuel, nor drive the tanker that filled the fuel tanks. He did not concoct the vanilla ice cream, add the mocha, nor did he freeze it or serve it. Thousands of people were responsible for the design and construction of the aircraft, and many more thousands were involved in preparing it for its journey. All our pilot did was come to a ready-made machine, and perform the task for which he is well trained. While in no way wishing to minimize or denigrate his crucial task, he is just the final cog in a coordinated exercise involving thousands of people. He should be the one giving the thanks to all those who made his flight possible.

Jewish people in particular are required to learn to appreciate the totality of the good that is done to them, and not simply look at the end result. (See for example the *Gemara* [*Berachos* 58a] which defines a good guest as the one who maximizes the praise due to the host almost to the point of exaggeration.) To look at something in isolation, and see nothing behind it, is to be guilty of myopia. Take for example a cup of coffee. What could be simpler? You wake up in the morning, trudge down the stairs (post-*negel vasser* etc...!), and with a mouth as dry as the Sahara desert, instinctively reach for the kettle and switch on. Spoon in the coffee, add boiling water, milk and sugar to taste — in three minutes you have the perfect drink. The *berachos* before and after are recited as a matter of course. Grateful? Why, sure. What do you want me to do, recite a sonnet? Compose a symphony? It's just a cup of coffee!

Just a cup of coffee. Did you know that the French author Balzac drank his coffee black, cold and thick as soup to keep him awake while writing through the night? The French philosopher (nothing personal against the French, it's only that their famous people had strange tastes) Voltaire drank an estimated 72 cups a day, and Beethoven is said to have used 60 beans for every cup. Nowadays, the coffee-drinking public prefer their coffee milder and instant. Before you reach for the coffee jar, try to calculate for a second just how many people were involved in your familiar cup of coffee. There's an awful lot of coffee in Brazil. And an awful lot of people are involved in the cultivation of the coffee plantations. The beans then have to be picked, packed and loaded onto ships to take them to the thirsty consumers. Ships, unlike the beans, do not grow on trees, and need to be built. Thousands more people are involved.

Now for the water. Coffee without water somehow doesn't taste as good. How does the water arrive at your tap? Another multitude of people are involved in the water industry. How do you heat the water; do you perhaps light a candle beneath it? Please come back tomorrow for your hot water! How many people are involved in the gas and electric industries?

But we're still not done. The cup from which you drink most probably did not fall from the sky, so add to your total the complete china and pottery — not to mention paper, plastic, and styrofoam — industries. Milk and sugar? Unless you grow your own sugar in your backyard, and Daisy the cow is a *bas bayis*, family member, you are reliant on the dairy industry and the huge sugar refineries. Don't forget the metal teaspoon (why it is not called a coffee spoon is one of the unsolved mysteries of mankind), the glass jar, the paper label, the transport, advertising and retail industries involved. Add it all together and you will find that a good proportion of the inhabitants of the world are directly involved in enabling you to enjoy your morning cup of coffee.

Perhaps not a round of applause, but certainly deserving of a sincere thank you!

And how about you yourself! Several times each day we recite a *berachah* to thank Hashem *Yisbarach* for the ability to eliminate waste. The duty sounds simple enough. Visit the bathroom, wash your hands, and say the *berachah*. Even if the ability was a simple one, we would have to be grateful. After all, even if you think that a cup of coffee is nothing more than a cup of coffee, you still have to show gratitude. The more you know about the plane, the more you are aware of the myriads involved in your coffee, the greater the obligation of gratitude. If we would realize that the ability to visit the bathroom is not just one simple action, but the culmination of many systems, each one more spectacular than the next (think perhaps of the urge to drink, the ability to swallow liquids, the capacity to digest liquids, and then gather the waste in a specific area ready for elimination), with each one involving millions of components, then the *berachah* would be some *berachah!*

A car emits exhaust fumes. A heating furnace gives off

smoke and soot. These are waste products. The body produces wastes, too. Most body wastes are end products of chemical reactions that are carried out in cells (of which you have a trillion) as the cells build up new substances and break down old ones. Examples of wastes include urea, containing broken-down proteins, and creatinine, produced when muscles contract. These wastes are collected by a special messenger — the blood — the body's main transport system. They are filtered and removed from the blood as it flows through the two kidneys in the lower back. The kidneys, bladder, and connecting tubes make up the urinary system. The kidneys receive a huge blood flow — up to 440 gallons each day. Each kidney has a million tiny filtering units, called *nephrons*, which extract wastes from blood to form urine.

Simple? A series of various-size pores in the nephron microfilters retain selected chemicals — according to the size, shape and other features of their molecules — and allow other chemicals to pass through. Red blood cells are big, and so do not pass into the filtering system at all. Urea passes through all filtering stages and ends up in urine. Glucose, salts, and other essential chemicals are first filtered out, but then wondrously reabsorbed into the blood in another part of the kidney in a system of microscopic tubes. The kidneys of an adult produce on average nearly two pints of urine each day. The exact amount is controlled by hormones. These adjust the filtering and water-absorbing rates of the kidneys. If you have plenty to drink, the kidneys produce a lot of dilute urine, so that the excess water is disposed of. If you drink only a small amount, the kidneys do not expel much water, so the waste material is more concentrated. Consider the enormous kindness of the design that allows a person to hold back the flow of waste even when the reservoir is full. Not for nothing is there a strong ring of muscle at the base of the reservoir (*urethral sphincter*) which safeguards both dignity and cleanliness. Consider that the reservoir is constructed of special cells that allow it to expand, and contains muscle to force out the liquid when signaled to do so. This is no simple storage container!

We are the pilots of a plane which is composed of millions of components and complex systems. We are the drinkers of coffee brought to us by courtesy of millions of people. When we give a moment's thought to the wonders that go on around us and within us, then the *berachah* is some *berachah!*

Moishe the Vasser Tregger

et your mind take you back to life in the *alter heim* (old homestead). Deep in the heartland of Eastern Europe, the little village nestles amongst the dense forests. There would be a muddy main street, with wooden sidewalks, simple wooden houses with low roofs, the general store that would sell everything from sacks of beans to shovels, and smoke from the wood fires would curl lazily from the tilting chimneys. Can you see the inhabitants? There is the venerable *Rav,* whose reputation has spread much further than the geographical boundaries of the small *shtetl;* Reb

Yankel the *Melamed*, forever surrounded by a cluster of children; and Moishe the *Vasser Tregger* (water carrier). Moishe was not born old, but in your mind's eye he is always elderly, bowed by the constant burden of the yoke of the two heavy buckets. Imagine that you lived in this idyllic setting. It might not be so idyllic when you begin to realize that your sole water supply was Moishe the *Vasser Tregger*. Your total daily water supply would be two bucketfuls, and none at all on Shabbos (or Yom Tov — sometimes three days in a row) or when Moishe did not feel up to it. Perhaps the good old days were not so good!

How things have changed! One hundred years ago, the average household used two buckets of water each day. Today? Would you believe that your modern household consumes about half a ton? On average, each of us uses 33 gallons of water every single day. We use it for baths and showers, drinking, cooking, washing clothes, watering the plants and cleaning the car. Imagine Moishe carrying half a ton of water to every household each day! Instead, bring the devoted Moishe into your home, and just show him how the water is delivered. Go to the faucet, turn it on and watch the water gush out. Not only is it seemingly limitless, but it has passed through a full treatment process. (It was not always so. In the last century, people were warned "not to work with any sort of water unless it has stood for two or three days, for when newly drawn it is always thick and muddy and needs to settle." Imagine waiting three days for a glass of water!)

From where does all the wonderful water come? Rainwater is stored in huge reservoirs, then purified in water-treatment works. There it is filtered, purified and disinfected. The clean water is then stored in large tanks. Then, through a network of pipes which snake underground, water arrives under pressure to your home. The enormous convenience of the modern water supply costs millions of dollars. It requires pumps, pipes and plastic; it needs the teamwork of geologists, engineers, chemists and laborers. Back in the *shtetl*, who would have dreamed that such advances would be possible? Would

Moishe have thought that there would be a time when his stalwart services would be obsolete! Go tell them, Moishe, that there is nothing new about their modern water-distribution system. Tell them that it has been happening for centuries, in fact, ever since the world was created, and tell them that their sophisticated system is really quite primitive in comparison to that of plants. Plants use and need an enormous amount of water. Most plants make their own food from water and air with the help of sunlight. This is the miracle of *photosynthesis.* Plants take water out of the soil, deliver it to their cells for use, and empty the remaining water into the air. Did you know that a crop of corn releases enough water during its life span to cover the field where it grows to a depth of nearly one foot! In the same way, plants change water and carbon dioxide into oxygen to manufacture substances which become food for us. You might like to know that a cucumber is 95 percent water, a pineapple 87 percent, a potato 80 percent and a tomato is also a top squelcher at 95 percent water. It is clear that an adequate water supply is nothing less than a matter of life itself for humans, animals, and plants.

Everyone knows that when you plant a seed in the earth, amazing things start happening. A seed is a tiny life-support package. Inside it is an embryo, which consists of the basic parts from which the seedling will develop, together with a supply of food. The food is needed to keep the embryo alive and fuel the process of germination. It is needed, so it is there! For weeks, months, or even years, the seed may remain inactive. (In 1933 a Japanese botanist found some lotus seeds in a dried-out lake bed in Manchuria. He sent them to the Royal Botanic Gardens at Kew, in London, where they were placed on moist blotting paper, and they sprouted into new plants. These seeds were later found to be hundreds of years old. We think it rather special that we can preserve food in our freezers for months. A seed doesn't think it is in any way special that it preserves its food for centuries!) But then, when the conditions are right, it suddenly comes alive and begins to grow. Whichever way the seed is placed in the ground, as it germinates the roots grow downwards, and the shoot begins to grow upwards. As the shoot grows upwards, it is hook shaped to prevent damage to the tip. Never do the roots grow up, nor the shoots down. Try explaining that! The seed and its diminutive stem might be tiny, but they are mighty strong. When plants grow, they can exert enormous pressure. Some seedlings can easily push through the tar on the surface of a new road, and can penetrate concrete! Try explaining that! As soon as the stem breaks ground, and is above the soil, it straightens up and reaches for the light. When the first leaves are opened, the seedling is now able to produce its own food by photosynthesis. Its days of dependence on the food reserves of the seed are over.

In the meantime, the roots have not been idle. Deeper and deeper they dive, thicker and thicker they grow. As a root grows, other smaller roots branch off from it, helping to absorb water and nutrients, and anchoring the plant in the ground. There is not a molecule anywhere on the plant that does not proclaim its design and wisdom! All roots have a cap of slimy cells at their tip. These cells prevent the roots from being worn away as they grow through the ground. A drill bit designed to penetrate metal will not be covered with cotton wool, but with the toughest tungsten, to prevent the tip from being worn away. Great design — learned from the roots of a humble plant.

It's all very well to spread roots into the ground, the source of water and nutrients, but how is the water and food going to be absorbed into the plant? You can sit in a kitchen surrounded by food, but if you have no mouth to eat, it isn't going to help you too much. Similarly, if you have a mouth, but all the food is in cans, and you don't possess a can opener, it might be just a little frustrating. If this plant wants to live, then everything has to work, and work well. It does! The secret of how water enters the roots of a plant is a process called *osmosis*. Osmosis can be understood as a movement of water from a weaker to a stronger solution. If two solutions (let us say one with a strong solution of salt, and one with a weak solution) were in contact, the water molecules would move one way, and the salt molecules the other until both were evenly distributed. If, however, the two solutions were separated by a membrane that allows water molecules to pass through more easily than salt, water will move out of the weak solution more rapidly than salt will move into it. Now look at the plant. Water is drawn into the root from the surrounding soil. The root hairs help by increasing the surface area. the concentration of salts in the root hairs is greater than that in the soil water, enabling the water to be drawn in through osmosis.

Do you think we know everything? The simplest plants are more complex than we can understand. For example: In living things, molecules and ions are sometimes pumped across the cell membrane. This is called active transport. No one knows exactly how it takes place, but the plant does require energy for it to happen. This is how plant roots obtain some of their mineral salts from the soil. Once in the plant, the water rises up the stem partly by being pushed from below, and partly by being pulled from above. The pushing force can be shown by cutting a stem near its base, where water will ooze out of the "wound" for a long time. The roots actually act as a pump. The pull from above is created by the evaporation of water from the leaf. If you stop this pulling force by, for example, cutting off the leaves, the passage of water up the stem is slowed down. This is why little water is taken up by deciduous trees in winter when they drop their leaves.

Inside the plant runs an impressive transport system. Flowering plants are busy throughout the day and night. During the hours of daylight, the leaves collect the sun's energy. This energy is then used to create food. The precious food supply has to be transported away from the leaves to the places where it is needed. At the same time, water and minerals have to be transported in the opposite direction to the farthest stems and branches. Water, minerals, and sugars are carried up and down a plant in bundles of tubelike cells. One system, called the *xylem*, carries water and minerals upwards. Another, called the *phloem*, can carry sugars either upwards or downwards to the parts that need them. The two systems are completely different, with vastly varying cell structures, and provide just a small insight into a complex and sophisticated transport system.

Moishe, tell them how the plants not only deliver water through their internal plumbing system, but food and minerals too. And they think that their faucet that delivers water is the last word in sophistication! Tell them that if they wish to see limitless wisdom and real design, they should look at a plant. The more wisdom we see in the design the more we appreciate the Designer. Thank you, Moishe the *Vasser Tregger*, for your important lesson. And thank you, Hashem *Yisbarach*, for Your fantastic world!

Bang Your Head Against the Wall

There is no doubt about it; it happens to be true. Please don't feel offended, the person might be you. One of the most popular words in the expressive Yiddish language is the word "*nudnik*." Even more popular than the word are the examples of the word. One classic *nudnik* is someone, who, when you ask innocently, "How are you?", spends the next half an hour telling you. Another *nudnik* is someone who phones you at 2 o' clock in the morning, and asks, "Did I wake you?" He is definitely related to the fellow who happens to know that your second cousin, who you hardly know, had a baby two weeks ago, and celebrates the fact by shouting "*Mazel Tov*" to you from his place on the other side of *shul*, causing everyone to come and ask you, "What's the big *mazel tov*?" Another species of *nudnik* is the one who asks questions which drive everyone mad. If you drop a pot of *cholent*, ruining an expensive carpet, he will ask in his infuriatingly disarming manner, "Why does *cholent* fall downwards rather than upwards?" He can never understand why it is that glaring looks are always being thrown in his direction. Another favorite question from this rare breed is one which has actually been heard. "Why is it," he asks with genuine curiosity, "that the *challah* knife can cut through the *challah*, but *challah* can never cut through the knife?"

In truth, although this type of question drives people crazy, it is quite legitimate. If you would never observe simple phenomena (like the fact that eyebrows remain the same length; that the ears of the listener are usually level with the mouth of the speaker, much more convenient than if the ears would have been close to the ground), you would never discern wisdom and design in the Creation. Similarly, if you did not have the type of mind that asks irritating questions, you would never invent anything. Many inventions appear so simple that we take them for granted. For example, before there were zippers, buttons or other fasteners, people fastened their clothes with large pins. But pins caused problems. Their sharp points were dangerous, and could easily slip out causing injury. What are you going to do — go and invent something! Listen to an interesting story. Walter Hunt was an American who thought up many inventions, which he usually patented. Since a patent application normally included drawings, and Mr. Hunt could not draw, he had to employ the services of an artist, to whom he was usually in debt. The artist agreed to wipe out the debts if Walter Hunt would give him sole rights to whatever he could make out of a length of old wire. Hunt came up with the safety pin, and the artist became a rich man!

Inventions may seem simple, once they have been invented.

Woody the Woodpecker. How would you like to bang your head against the wall?

But analyze any invention that you like, from a safety pin to a zipper (first patented in 1893), and perforce you will admit that without a great deal of inquisitiveness coupled with intelligence, they would never have seen the light of day. In that case, you will appreciate the following problem. Sometimes you need to hang a picture on the wall, and you cannot find the hammer, let alone nails, and your neighbor borrowed the ladder, and naturally failed to return it. Could you please invent a method whereby you can climb up the wall without a ladder, grip the wall securely with your feet, and bang a hole into the wall with your nose? You will react with disbelief, and quite rightly too. I can understand that wood can be fashioned into a ladder, and metal into a drill, but that you should be able to transform yourself into both a flying creature and a human drill, simultaneously, sounds like something from science fiction. Is such a thing possible?

Not only possible, but so common that — like the humble safety pin — it is almost taken for granted. Enter the woodpecker. Woodpeckers are the only creatures who spend most of their waking hours banging their heads against wood. They do this because of the role that they have been given in the animal world, gleaning insects from under the bark of trees. They have the rare distinction of being the only living things able to locate and eradicate these insect hordes. First, let us respect the woodpecker for its vital role. It is tremendously important to the woodland economy, for it strips dead trees of their bark and prevents the spread of carpenter-ant colonies to sound trees nearby. It is also unbelievably efficient. A large woodpecker once removed 30 feet of bark in less than 15 minutes; and its appetite matches its efficiency. Examination of the stomach contents of one bird revealed 2,600 carpenter ants!

Every part of the woodpecker's body is directed toward the sole object of hewing wood. Its legs are short and powerful, and they grasp the bark by a unique arrangement of sharply pointed toes — two toes point forward, two backward, forming a gripping pair of tongs on each foot. So there you are — if you want to climb the wall without a ladder, just tell your body to please comply and grow a pair of wings, and then to rearrange its toes in the manner described. If the woodpecker can do it, why can't you? The woodpecker's tail sits firmly against the tree trunk, acting as a brace, propping and steadying the bird as it delivers jackhammer blows with its bill. The middle pair of those tail feathers is unusually strong, and remarkably, these feathers, which are the main props, do not fall out during molting until all the other tail feathers have been replaced and can support the weight of the bird. You really do not have to look hard for evidence of design in anything; you just have to open your eyes and it's all there for you to see.

And now for the biggest problem of all. Try (in your imagination) to slam your head against an unyielding wall. Once will give you a headache, twice a migraine, three times a severe concussion. How about banging your head against the wall at the rate of 100 times a minute? How would you protect the main computer (the brain) from irreparable damage? Woodpeckers experience no problem. You will never find woodpeckers with concussions lying dazed at the foot of the tree, nor have there ever been any, for the little bird is perfectly equipped for slamming its head against wood without any injury whatsoever.

The beak is straight, very hard and pointed. The skull that drives it is unusually thick and is moved by powerful neck muscles. Now for the amazing part. The bones between the beak and skull are not rigidly joined, as they are in most other birds. Instead, the connective tissue is spongy and elastic, serving as a shock absorber. When you bear in mind that shock absorbers were not introduced into moving vehicles until well into this century, it becomes apparent that a system of shock absorbers built into the head is anything but simple. (By the way, don't feel left out, for you too have shock absorbers in your heel which cushion the impact of running down the road.)

The wonders have not ended. The woodpecker's ability to locate insects is uncanny, and for this it has been endowed with an acute sense of hearing. After the bird taps on the trunk, it pauses a moment, waiting to hear whether the tapping has disturbed any insects hidden inside. Once a bird has found a place where the sound indicates that further investigation is necessary, its taps become sharper. Then, as it zeros in on the insects, the bark begins to fly. Woodpeckers have an uncanny skill for gauging the strength of the wood in which they find their feast, and in which they nest. More than half the weight of the tree trunk may be above their excavation, yet they dig the hole in such a way that it does not place a strain on the tree. Rain and wind are kept out of their nest by drilling the entry passage upward before turning downward to hollow out the long, vertical nesting cavity. Do you have any idea who taught them these advanced building and engineering skills?

Of all the tools in its small body, the woodpecker's tongue is the most remarkable. Very long — in some cases four times as long as the beak — the tongue can be flicked in and out like a snake's. The tongue is pliable and dexterous, and is able to wind itself around the curves and bends of the insect galleries. Examine its tongue closely (but not too closely) and you will see that it is pointed and has barbs on the tip like little fishhooks. It is used to impale grubs and pull them out of their galleries. In addition, the tip of the tongue is coated with a sticky substance. It uses its sticky tongue as bait to catch ants; the ants rush forward to attack what appears to be a worm climbing into their nest, and there they remain, stuck to the hungry woodpecker's tongue. One species of woodpecker is unique in the way it obtains its food. It drills a series of small holes close together into the bark of trees, and licks the fountains of sap. The fountains also attract insects, which are then added to the diet without the necessity of drilling for them!

Because of their wondrous equipment, woodpeckers can dig out insects both in winter and summer; consequently their migrations are of limited range. Many survive the winter by living on acorns and nuts which they have stored. In California particularly, the acorn-storing woodpecker methodically studs the bark of trees with close rows of holes, into each of which it tightly taps an acorn. Embedded in one giant pine tree were acorns estimated to total at least 50,000; enough to support many sons-in-law, with enough remaining to make a grand *melaveh malkah!*

Never be afraid of being described as a *nudnik*. If you don't observe, and you don't ask unusual questions, your mind will remain so closed to the wonders of the Creator that fill the universe that not even the woodpecker will be able to open it.

The Dam Builders

Everyone loves a *kiddush*. Since the *kiddush* comes immediately after *davening* on Shabbos morning, we love it even more. Especially at a Bar Mitzvah, when the *davening* is a little longer, the *leining* a lot longer (big family, everyone of whom needs an *aliyah* with a *misheberach* to ensure relative harmony), the thought and aroma of the creamy cakes and other culinary delights as the marathon performance draws to a close is enough to make the pangs of hunger a palpable force. As the famished congregants make their way slowly and sedately from the

Dam built by 40,000 men. Almost as good as …

shul to the adjoining hall, the threat of being trodden in the human avalanche is real! Imagine that you, *tzaddik* that you are, wish to teach patience to the hungry crowd. You position yourself in the doorway, your arms and legs spread-eagled across the opening, and stop. At first you hear impatient "*Nu's*." Then the level of "*Nu's*" increases. The strain on your back, as 200 hungry people push forward, is difficult to withstand. Desperately you hold your position, the force increases until finally the sheer pressure of the crowd washes you away like a twig in a raging river. It was a brave, but futile try.

... dams built by one beaver.

If holding back people is difficult, what would you say about restricting the passage of surging water? Everyone has heard of, or seen, dams. Dams allow water to be stored in reservoirs, enabling the water supply to be controlled throughout the year. Water from a reservoir can be used to drive turbines which provide electricity. But how do you set about building a dam? You understand that dams have to withstand more pressure or weight than any other man-made structure. The massive Hoover Dam, on the Colorado River, is a colossal 577 feet high, and holds back 38 billion tons of water! In the 20th century, dam building represents the peak of engineering skill and imagination. It has produced structural forms as daring and as original as any the world has ever seen. You can choose between gravity dams (which rely on their weight to resist the horizontal force of the water), arch dams (which transfer the pressure of the water to the sides of the valley) or a combination of both, as in the celebrated Hoover Dam. Either way, the complexity and difficulties involved stagger the imagination. In 1988, the world's largest hydroelectric generating plant was completed after nearly 14 years of work by 40,000 men. This involved damming the River Parana, the fifth largest river in the world, which forms the border between Brazil and Paraguay. There is no doubt about it. You have to be clever to dam a river ...

... Sorry, there seems to be an interruption. I have a small creature here (two and a half feet long, a foot high, weighing 50 pounds) who seems a little agitated. He says that he's been damming rivers since he was created, and he doesn't understand what all the fuss is about! Speak up, Mr. Beaver!

Listen carefully and you will hear — Crash! The cool stillness of the forest is suddenly shattered by the sound of a young tree falling to the ground. A small, brown, furry creature scurries through the undergrowth and slips into the nearby river for safety. It waits there until it is sure that no enemies have been attracted by the noise, then returns to the tree. Its strong front teeth set to work gnawing through the branches, stripping the trunk bare. The North American beaver then grasps the trunk in its powerful jaws, and drags it into the water. The creature tugs and pushes the trunk into position amongst the mound of branches, twigs, mud and boulders which makes up its dam.

Pause for a moment, and examine the amazing structure of this most remarkable little animal. His back feet are webbed like a duck's, his forefeet are strong, and his little hands are agile, like a monkey's. He has a broad scaly tail, 10 inches in length and half as much in width which is used as a rudder when swimming, a prop when standing or sitting, and a transmitter of news. When a beaver scents danger, he spanks the water with his tail. On quiet days the ringing noise can be heard a quarter of a mile away, and every beaver within earshot will disappear. If you surprise a beaver on land, he will not fight. He will run for his pond, dive like an expert and swim like a champion. He possesses the ability to close his nose and his ears (you try it next time you take a bath!) and a transparent covering slides down over each eye to allow it to see underwater. Mr. Beaver relaxes his muscles, and drops his heartbeat by half, allowing him to remain underwater for 15 minutes. Each of these features is noteworthy in and of itself, for without it he could not survive.

But none are as extraordinary as its teeth. A beaver has 20 teeth. The four strong, curved front teeth (orange in color — it never brushes them!) are called incisors, and are used for gnawing through the trunks of trees. The 16 back teeth are used for chewing. Between the incisors and the back teeth are flaps of skin, one on each side of the beaver's mouth. These flaps fold inwards, and seal off the back of the mouth to prevent both splinters of wood and water from entering the beaver's lungs. Those long front teeth are covered with almost unbreakable enamel. (Before the advent of stainless steel, kitchen sinks were made of enamel and lasted forever.) Those front teeth (and only the front teeth) grow constantly, and he has to keep sawing in order to keep them at an acceptable length. Just think for a moment. Your front teeth stop growing when you are about 8 years old. Normal people do not chop down trees with their mouths, and so do not require the ever growing, constantly replenishing front-teeth saws. What would happen if you suddenly developed an insatiable appetite for the delicious bark of trees — would your teeth begin to grow? Would your children's teeth also continue growing? But it makes no sense. Why should front teeth continue growing, without the appetite for trees (imagine tripping over your front teeth!)? On the other hand, what use would an appetite for trees be without the specialized teeth to chew them. In any case, who says that a sudden interest in tree barks will trigger the growth of conveyor belt-style front teeth — perhaps your own human teeth are a little short, why not ask them to grow a little longer, surely they would oblige! Oh yes?! The whole story makes no sense whatsoever unless you say, as you suspected all along, that the little beaver is not the master of its own destiny, nor is it the designer of its own form. It was created from the outset with its very special front teeth to perform the task for which it is uniquely designed.

And how well it does its job! The beaver's logging operations are as amazing as his carpentry and engineering. Standing on his hind feet (using his tail as a support) he eats around a tree until what are going to be the stump and the falling tree appear like smooth, tapering spikes balanced point upon point. Either the wind or law of gravity finally bring the tree crashing. While they may prefer saplings, a tree 18 inches thick presents no problem. Why does Mr. Beaver need to fell trees ? Either for food, or to build the dam for which he has deservedly achieved such fame and renown. It is the icebound northern winter that makes a beaver build a dam. Winter means no open water to plunge into for refuge, and snow cover is difficult to travel through to find bark to eat. So our industrious beaver creates a personal pond, in whose muddy base he can anchor a whole winter's supply of eating timber, and on which he can build an impregnable mansion for himself and his family. He begins by felling a tree near a river, causing it to jam near the point where he intends to build. Once set, the tree catches silt and driftwood, and the beaver furiously lugs in material from the riverbanks; mud, sticks, stones, grass, which he works into one mass, to consolidate the emerging dam. Mud is the major ingredient, and is carried in his hands, and during his dives to the dam's foundations, he works it into place with his hands and the side of his face. He begins in the middle, and builds towards either shore.

How wide is his dam? Think big! It may be just 10 feet long, or more than 2,000. The record is a 2100 footer in the state of Montana, in the western United States. Once the dam is completed, and the water level established, the beaver then builds a home for his family, called a lodge. This lodge may be fixed to the dam, to the shore, or to an island in the pond. Its foundations are sticks, stones, and twigs, woven so professionally that it cannot dissolve or collapse. The dome-shaped lodge is built from branches, reeds and mud. There are two entrances, through the floor and under the water. One acts as an escape hatch if submersible enemies enter to pay an unexpected and unwelcome call ! The top of the lodge, of heavily woven thatch, is not completed until freezing weather sets in. Then, the beaver plasters it thickly with mud, which freezes into an armor plate often 10 inches thick. Nothing that prowls (from a bear to a lynx) has the strength in its claws to tear through that roof.

The fact that beavers are sociable, peaceful, industrious and faithful to their families is interesting. The fact that they are fully equipped to chop down trees, build solid dams and intricate homes without the assistance of a single machine, simply using the specialized facilities that their bodies provide, is an inspiration. It is an inspiration because no amount of wishful thinking will enable you to grow a security tail, webbed feet, transparent eyelids, or self-replenishing teeth. Mr. Beaver, dam builder extraordinary, can thank the Creator Who designed and formed him with such wisdom. And we, the humans who observe it all, can use the minds with which we were created, to gain inspiration and learn *emunah*.

Color It Yellow

Revolutions do not have to be revolting. While it is true that the altercation that England had with its American colonies in 1775 was not too pleasant for the old country, and the rebellion in France in 1789 — which cost King Louis XVI his head and replaced the monarchy with a republic — was not pleasant for anyone, many other revolutions have been relatively painless. Take for example the revolution in travel. In the old days (even as recently as 50 years ago), travel was an ordeal, costly, and something to be avoided. If you lived in England, or in the

United States, and your cousin, or even your brother was getting married in *Eretz Yisrael*, it would not enter your mind to attend the wedding. In just half a short century, everything has changed dramatically. A man in England will think nothing of telling his *chavrusah* that he'll be away for a couple of days, because he has to "run over" to *Eretz Yisrael* for a *simchah*. Flying over the Atlantic has become as commonplace as crossing a river.

Another revolution, which also has been painless and subtle, has been the revolution in book covers. Think of an old library or any *sefarim* more than 30 years old, and the picture that your mind conjures up is one of drab, colorless *sefarim*. Like Henry Ford's Model "T," you could have any color as long as it was black. The *sefarim* in English, the few that existed, were little better. The titles were dull and uninteresting, the colors bland and dreary, and to the casual peruser, the contents gave the impression of being heavy and humorless. The visitor to the *sefarim* store would have needed to be of a dedicated breed, and would have had to know precisely which *sefer* he wanted, for they all looked identical. No longer! A visit to a modern *sefarim* store has become a positive pleasure. The colors jump at you. The designs are imaginative, alive, clever, and above all attractive. Whether in English or Hebrew, the print of *sefarim* is clear and pleasing to the eye. The book covers are vibrant, bold and individualized and give you *cheshek* to pick them up and read them. We have not yet reached the stage where book titles come brilliantly illuminated in miniature neon-lighting, flashing on and off in their gaudy colors, although experience warns us that we have not come to the end of the line!

What has changed? What caused the revolution? Probably nothing more than a desire to sell more books. You could be philosophical and say that people are more superficial, are attracted by anything that glitters, but the truth remains that if something is well packaged, it will attract the eye. What attracts the eye will make the heart desire, and by that time you have bought the book! Color a book plain brown with a bland insipid title — it could be brilliantly written and filled with gems of knowledge — no one will even pick it up. Whoever designs book covers has engaged in some market research, and has discovered what it is that attracts potential customers. He knows that those buyers are humans, just like himself, and that the human species has eyes. He knows that those eyes can see in color, and are attracted by bright, cheerful colors. The revolution in packaging, which has been applied in all sectors of retailing, from breakfast cereal to baby food, from peanut butter to diapers, has done nothing more than apply the lessons that have been all around us since the world began. Take, for example, …

… The banana. You do not have to be a genius to know that the Designer of bananas definitely wanted them to be eaten. They are wholesome, nutritious, low in cholesterol, and the original convenience food. The packaging is simply superb. Take them anywhere, on your travels, for your lunch, or in your office for a snack. They are clean, dry, virtually odorless, and remain fresh for many days (by the time you buy them in the stores they have probably been off the tree for several weeks). Whenever you fancy eating your banana, you need neither a stove nor a microwave, neither a can opener nor a knife. Just peel off the waterproof protective skin, and eat. No cooking, roasting or pickling required. A ready to eat, nutritious, healthy meal — the original (and the best) convenience food. What is it that attracts you to the banana? It cannot be the aroma, for it has none, at least not till after it has hit its prime. It is unlikely to be its unusual shape, because a cucumber lacks the banana's curve, yet people do eat cucumbers. Is it its striking bright yellow color which captures the eye? But how did the banana know that humans, who eat bananas, have color sight — or for that matter have eyes at all? Well, there you are, it would appear that the Designer of the banana knew His customers, and knew all about their eyesight and taste buds, and well He might, for He designed those too.

Yellow says hello, bright for your sight. A gleaming bright yellow *sefer* will most certainly capture your attention. If so, why are not all *sefarim* colored yellow? Sunglasses supplied at the door of the store, and shelf upon shelf of sunshine, a luminous array of buttercup and lemon, gold, topaz and amber! The answer is variety. If every *sefer* was yellow, they would fail to attract. That is the nature of man. He can eventually become bored even with the most beautiful and precious. (What is your favorite cake? You enjoy it, don't you! Imagine how you would feel if you were compelled to eat it for breakfast, lunch and supper, day after monotonous day, week after excruciating week, month after unbearable month! Funny thing is that no cow has ever been known to protest about the monotony of its diet — just grass, grass, and now, for an exciting change — grass. Cows don't mind, sheep don't complain, goats have never rebelled! There seems to be something special about humans that make them innately dissatisfied, always wanting something new, different, varied.) Knowing the eccentricities of their customers, book designers vary their colors. Blue cover with green writing, green cover with gold lettering, red cover with yellow title — as long as it is new, eye catching, and different.

And different they most certainly are. Tomatoes need to be eaten. Their survival depends on it! All their future generations lie inside, waiting patiently to be spread afield to begin a new branch of the family. Each tiny seed is encased in a slippery container to guarantee it safe passage through the hazardous human digestive system, perhaps to find a fertile patch on which to set down roots. If so, the tomato cannot rely on the altruism of mankind — it has to attract it! Why not bright yellow? No, it has to be something different. Bright red. Nothing is as ostentatious as crimson red. There you are, Mr. Human — can you see me, cheerful and sweet — absolutely irresistible.

It is not only people who need people. Peaches need people too. Without the human to eat the peach, and break their teeth on the stone, the stone would never be thrown away.

That is exactly what the peach parent wants — for in that impregnable fortress of a stone lies its precious child, waiting patiently for someone to hurl it to the ground (where a special enzyme in the earth has been prepared to dissolve the seal which holds together the two halves of the stone), allowing the seed to begin a fresh generation. How can Mr. Peach attract the crucial sight of humans? Bright red or bright yellow? No, we need something special. How about a blushing blend of golden yellow, gentle orange, and delicate pink? There you have yourself a winner. When people behold you with their eyes, they will attest that they have never ever seen anything so beautiful. The Designer, knowing mankind's power of sight, his preferences in taste, and his likes in each of his senses, has taken this subtle dream of colors, painted them on a canvas of velvet, and created within them a food which is a chef's dream of good taste and sweetness. When you consider the thought and care which has been invested in the production of this fruit, are you surprised that it is a worldwide best seller?

(In stark contrast, have you ever heard of truffles — much liked in France? Truffles are the fruits of a fungus that grows only in a strange partnership with tree roots. The fungus takes food from the tree, but makes some nutrients in the soil available to the tree in return. Now truffles rely on animals to dig them up, eat them, and spread the seeds in that which they eliminate. How do you attract an animal to dig you up? The amazing answer is that these truffles produce some of the same odors that animals themselves make! The design demonstrated by this example of cooperation and inter-dependence between fruit and consumer just staggers the imagination!)

Most amazing of all is that these wonderful arrays of color and texture, shape and taste, all come from the cold dark clammy earth. The alchemists of old used to huddle over their cauldrons, employing a mixture of magic and astrology, muttering incantations and mysterious spells in their vain attempt to change base metal into gold. They never succeeded.

To transform worthless metal into shining gold would be child's play when contrasted with that which the Master Chemist performs. Graphic designers have revolutionized the book trade in making *sefarim* so attractive. Their revolution, however, is not original, rather a replica of the design incorporated into the world when Hashem *Yisbarach* created the world, together with its fantastic fruits and vegetables.

Not Just Dry Bones

"Look before you leap" is a famous proverb. "A miss is as good as a mile" is proverbial too. It is the brevity and simplicity of the proverb that gives it its endurance, but its simplicity is very often deceptive. You try and make one! It is not as easy as it seems. The same could be said for many inventions. Take a bicycle. It seems such a simple invention, one which we are happy to take for granted. There are no complicated mechanical processes involved, just a couple of wheels and a pedaling device. Wheels have been around for as long as anyone can remember, and there is no logical reason why Julius Caesar should not have charged up the beaches of England in the year 55 on his mountain bike when he decided to invade. He had all the technology at his disposal. It was just that no one thought of it. Despite the simplicity of the design, the bike has only been with us for about 150 years, advancing from the simplest design to our modern machines.

Could you possibly think of anything simpler than a paper clip? It seems the simplest invention of all; a short length of bent wire that holds papers together. Again, wire has been with us for centuries (indeed it was when someone was holding a bunch of wires, and removed one, that he first discovered a wireless) and there is no reason why the pieces of paper that constituted the United States Constitution should not have been held together with a ceremonial paper clip. But it was not. People used to hold their papers together with pins, which could damage the papers and give the user a nasty prick! It was not until the early years of this century that the first patent was filed for the wire paper clip, and now it would be safe to bet that there isn't a desk drawer in the land that does not have at least one paper clip lurking in the corner.

It is when we realize our limitations in inventing even the simplest device (could you invent a machine that pairs socks, or perhaps one that allows a schoolchild to write five lines simultaneously? If you can, your fame and fortune is guaranteed!) that we can begin to appreciate the wisdom and intelligence inherent in the design of the human body. Take your very own bones for example. Bones support and protect. Your muscles, intestines, blood vessels and other vital organs would collapse into a soggy heap if it were not for the body's supporting framework, which we call the skeleton. In the olden days, bones were likened to the stone columns and wooden beams of a building. They were thought of as lifeless internal supports, that simply held up all the floppy parts of the body. However, as the science of anatomy advanced, the view of bones gradually changed. It was realized that bones in the body are not dry and brittle, but that up to one third of a bone is water, that bones are slightly soft and flexible, and that they have their own blood vessels and nerves, like any other organ. The men of science found out that bones are alive, that they use energy and nutrients, and they can detect sensations. Not quite a wooden beam and stone column!

Have you ever walked through a train? Have you ever seen someone recklessly stand between two cars while the train is moving? If you place one foot on one side of the connecting section, and the other foot on the other side, you will have realized that although the cars are connected (this is done to ensure that all the passengers arrive at their destination), the coupling that connects them is flexible. Were this not the case, the train would buckle and bend as it went around a corner. It is your spine that allows you to stand erect. The spine is composed of 29 separate bones, which are called vertebrae. Imagine if those bones were connected to each other in such a way that they touched. Can you picture the agony of grinding bones that would ensue every time you wanted to bend your back? If vertebra ground on vertebra, absorbing solid jolts with every step that you take, the whole structure would not last too long. Can you invent something quickly?

Fortunately, we have been provided with a cushion between each vertebra. These cushions are called discs, and are made of cartilage. Cartilage is a smooth and glossy substance, which is also rubbery and tough. It also has the good fortune of being relatively soft. You will find it in your voice box (your vocal cords are made of it), and if you touch your nose and pull your ear, there you will also find cartilage. The discs between the vertebrae act as shock absorbers and allow the spine to bend in any direction. Each disc consists of a wide rim of cartilage containing a resilient jellylike interior substance. The discs are thickest where they have to bear the greatest weight, in the lower

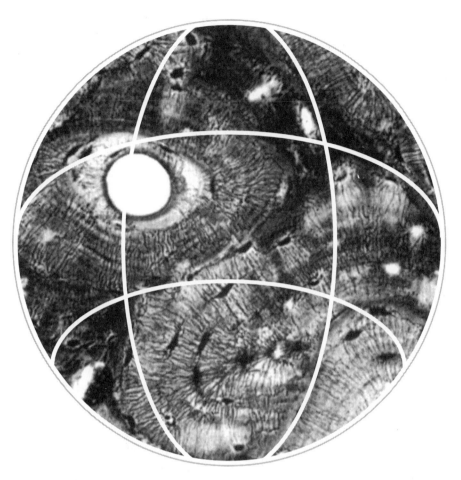

A Haversian system – advanced technology that staggers the mind.

lumbar region. Think what amount of foreknowledge goes into the production of a jelly doughnut, or a car's shock absorber, and you will begin to appreciate the insight and sagacity, not to mention the kindness, that the discs demonstrate. Nothing happens by itself!

What really takes the breath away is the actual structure of the bones themselves. The highly flexible, constantly moving, internal scaffolding is designed to work nonstop for 120 years. Most structure built by humans (washing machines, cars, houses) deteriorate with constant use. Bones, on the other hand, become stronger and more resilient with reasonable amounts of exercise and activity, and regular use actually encourages the joints to remain supple and healthy for longer than they would if they were inactive. Structural engineers have long acknowledged the combination of strength and lightness given by bone. Pound for pound, bone is stronger than wood, concrete or steel. (Doesn't that give you *nachas*? It's like hearing that a close member of your family has won the lottery!) If the human skeleton were made of enough steel to equal the strength of bone, it would weigh five times as much. The strength of bone comes from its design. The Italian physicist Galileo, who lived in the 16th century, knew that if hollow tubes and solid rods are both made from the same weight of material, the hollow tube is stronger. Following the same principle, the long, slim bones in the body's limbs, such as the thighbone (femur), are not solid rods, but tubes, with hollow chambers along their shafts. This makes them both light and strong.

Let's take a closer look. The bone tissue in the bones is made of fibers of the protein *collagen,* which give it elasticity, and of mineral crystals, which make it hard. That, however is not enough. The direction in which the fibers are laid is of vital importance. They are all arranged in circular patterns! Listen to this amazing discovery. The inner structure of the bone is built up from thousands of compactly arranged tube-shaped units, each called a *Haversian system.* The units are named after an English physician, Mr. Clopton Havers, who published his bone studies in 1691. A Haversian system is only one hundredth of an inch (0.25 millimeter) in diameter. It is made from thousands of fibers of collagen, embedded in mineral salts of calcium and phosphorus. The fibers are laid in circular layers, like the growth rings you see in a sliced-through tree trunk.

The principle works in this way. When engineers work on the design for a large structure, such as a skyscraper, they know that the strength of the building material to be used is only one consideration. Other factors are the shape, size and arrangement of main supporting parts, such as steel girders or concrete pillars. A structure may have a good supporting capacity even if its individual structural parts are quite weak. This fact was known to the Designer of bones. You can actually try it out. If you would take drinking straws, and stick them into a flat disk of clay so that they point in all directions, then make a second tower with the same number of straws placed upright in a circular pattern, and then tested them for strength by pressing a book on them, the random arrangement would quickly collapse, whereas the ring-of-straws design is much stronger. And there is more. The arrangement of Haversian systems is only part of the bone's structural strength. These tube-shaped units are also stuck firmly to each other by something called bone matrix, which acts as a "living glue." This gives the bone its remarkable strength. In this manner, very strong structures can be built from lightweight materials. Would you have been able to work that all out by yourself? Even the simpler-than-simple paper clip was only invented 90 years ago, yet within your bones you incorporate systems of such advanced technology that they stagger the mind.

If human inventiveness is limited, Divine wisdom is limitless. Your bones prove it. Bone has a great advantage over structural materials such as steel and concrete. If it breaks, it can mend itself. Healing of a fracture begins almost at once. Leaking blood from the broken bone forms a clot. After a few days, cells called *fibroblasts* and *osteoblasts* make an open network of spongy bone in the gap left by the break. A week or two later, the spongy bone gradually fills in and becomes harder. Blood vessels have regrown and healed. After two or three months, the bone is almost mended. The bulge at the break shrinks away due to the expert attention of specialist cells called *osteoclasts*, that actually destroy bone, trimming off rough edges, helping sculpture the bone back to its original shape.

Every single one of those processes is complex beyond belief, yet something we happily take for granted. The least we can do to demonstrate our gratitude is to stand straight, erect in posture, with all our bones, joints and muscles in their optimum position, and thank Hashem *Yisbarach* for the marvelous inventions that make it all possible.

"Baruch Atah Hashem ... Zokeif Kefufim"

Grand Hotel

Driving long distance is a tiring business. It is not so bad when the road twists and turns, for the variety in the road layout can act as a stimulant to keep the mind alert. Modern highways, however, are often long and unbending, and hours of monotonous conditions can cause fatigue and tedium. The best thing to help you keep awake is a talkative passenger. The need to listen, respond and reply to a human voice is the most effective antidote against the mind-numbing tiredness that is every driver's worst enemy. Conversely, a passenger who gives monosyllabic answers to questions, or one who thinks for 10 minutes before answering "Yes" or "No" is as useful as a tape case with the tape missing.

Even the most robust and energetic driver needs to stop for a rest on a long journey. The car needs gas and the driver also needs refueling. Fortunately, there are service stations located at regular intervals along the highway. Eager for your business, they advertise their presence well in advance — "Services Area 27 miles" — so that you have ample opportunity to make a decision to interrupt your journey. "We'll stop at the next service station. Everyone happy?"

You will notice that these establishments have been carefully designed. Besides offering the usual restroom facilities, they understand the needs of the driver and his passengers, and the services offered are in harmony with his needs. Here you will not find houses for sale, or even Shabbos shoes. Not on these premises will you be able to purchase a *chasunah* suit or even gardening equipment. Rather you will be offered fast food, cold drinks, coloring- and puzzle-books, motor oil and windshield wiper fluid. The decor is bright and breezy, airy and relaxing. A break, a breather, refuel and go. That's what the customers want, and, understanding their needs and wanting their business, the service stations are clever enough to provide it all. If you wish to succeed in any business, you have to discern the needs and likes of the customer and provide it. Failure to do so will lead to early closure. Service stations have found the winning formula.

They must have learned it from the flowers. As a shop relies on customers to succeed, so a flower relies on insects (or birds, or animals) to survive. You have to understand how it works. In order for a flower to produce seeds, it needs to be fertilized. For fertilization to take place, pollen grains have to travel from the anther (which produces pollen) to the stigma (which receives pollen). Some plants pollinate themselves, but most rely on receiving pollen from another plant of the same species. This is called cross-pollination. Pollen can be dispersed by wind (as sufferers of hay fever are painfully aware) or by water, but the most important pollinators are insects and birds. Contrary to popular belief, beautifully colored flowers have not been created to allow a forgetful husband the opportunity to make amends for neglecting his wife's birthday. The colorful petals of the flower are advertising billboards to their flying customers. Plants entice insects to their flowers by their bright colors, and by food in the form of nectar. While the visiting insect feeds, pollen from the anthers is pressed onto its back, often at a particular place, such as on the back or on the head. The stigma of the flower that receives the precious pollen is in just the right place to collect it as the insect arrives.

Just those bare facts by themselves would be quite sufficient to convince a thinking person that the plants know how to conduct business. They know their customers. But it goes far beyond that. No traveler will stop at a service station simply to keep them in business. There has to be an advantage to the customer, and the manager has to know both how to attract the customer and keep him there long enough to part with his hard-earned cash. No insect or bird will land on a plant and act as a pollen-deliverer purely *l'shem shamayim*. There has to be an attraction and an incentive. Insects have a very highly developed sense of smell (how else would the bees be aware of the presence of honey in your *succah?*) and have excellent vision. The plant employs beautifully decorated colors and the most exquisite of aromas to attract the eyes and nose of the insect, and the incentive to stay around awhile is the sweet nectar. The plant produces nectar in special factories, called nectaries, that are usually hidden deep in the depths of the flower. Positioning them in this way has two advantages. It reduces loss of nectar by evaporation or dilution by rain, and it compels a visiting messenger to brush past the anthers and so collect its load of pollen. But this reward has to be advertised. How is the insect to know where to go?

The service station has directions for cars, trailers and heavy trucks. Everyone uses their eyes and knows in which direction to steer their vehicles. The eyes of insects, however, are very different from ours in the perception of color. At the red end of the spectrum, the insect eye is not as sensitive as ours. Most insects are unable to distinguish between red and black as we can. At the other end, the blue end, they are very much more sensitive than we are and can detect ultraviolet colors that are totally invisible to us. Many flowers that are pollinated by insects, particularly those that conceal their nectaries (nectar storehouses), have dots and lines which lead from the outer lip, where an insect might land, to the nectar within. Foxgloves and irises, pansies and rhododendrons are good examples. These marks are guidelines in exactly the same way that we ourselves place markings on airport runways. If you see an evening primrose in normal light, it appears almost unmarked, but ultraviolet light reveals clear pointers to its reward of nectar.

On the other hand, plants that are pollinated by birds often have red or pink petals. Birds have excellent color vision, and a bright red flower, which also produces nectar, readily attracts them. A certain plant, called an urn plant, is found high up on trees. Because of its green neighbors, it needs to be conspicuous to attract the attention of its bird pollinators. Hence its bright red color. Most insects cannot see red, so it is an unusual color for insect-pollinated flowers.

The most highly specialized of all nectar-feeding birds are the South American hummingbirds. They can beat their wings so swiftly and position them so accurately that they can suspend themselves in the air in front of a flower. South American plants, in response, attract them with delicate flowers, suspended from the end of long thin stems, and facing outwards so that they can be entered only from the air. As it collects nectar, it is given a liberal dusting of pollen on its chin. Now listen to this. The rate at which this type of flower supplies its nectar has to be carefully controlled. If the plant is miserly and produces very little, a bird will not find it worthwhile to come visiting. If it is too generous, then the bird might be so satisfied after its visit that it will not hurry to seek more nectar elsewhere and so fail to deliver the pollen swiftly. The plants, therefore, maintain a perfect compromise between these two extremes. The hummingbirds pollinating them are compelled to keep continuously active, rushing from one flower to another, getting just enough each time to fuel their high-energy flying equipment with just sufficient calories left over to make the trip profitable. At night, when they cannot see to fly, and the flowers have closed, the birds have no alternative but to shut down all their systems, lower their body temperature, and, in effect, hibernate until dawn.

Let us pause for a chance to digest. What we have stated is that there is no difference whatsoever between the knowledge and intelligence demonstrated by the service station manager in attracting his customers and the knowledge and intelligence shown by plants in their need to survive. The plant "knows" that insects are partial to sweet substances, which in turn means that the plant is fully aware that insects have an acute sense of taste (did you know that?). In order to attract the insect, it needs to send out an aromatic and colorful signal advertising the presence of nectar, which in turn tells us that the plant is fully cognizant of the insect's ability to smell and see. The plant not only knows that insects and birds have color vision (how should they know that — many animals can only see in shades of grey!), but is privy to the secret that the insect can not see red, but is pretty adept at ultraviolet blue. In a manner no less skillful and intelligent than your local airport placing landing lights on the runway to guide in the planes, your little plant incorporates markings (in ultraviolet blue so that only the pollinating insects should notice them — unwanted guests are not welcome!) together with landing pads so that the insects should experience no difficulty in reaching its life-giving goal. This is no simple service station, it is nothing less than Grand Hotel complete with heliport! Where does all this intelligence come from? How is it that the plant is in possession of all these facts whereas you, with your super-intelligent brain, knew nothing before you began reading this article? The answer is that in precisely the same way that your computer is a fantastic machine capable of amazing skills, but all the intelligence that it possesses comes not from itself but from an outside source of superior intelligence (in this case mankind), so all the "knowledge" and "intelligence" demonstrated so visibly and clearly by any plant that you choose does not come from itself, but rather from an outside source. Intelligence does not come from a void, nor does it come by accident. The outside source is the Supreme Intelligence Who created Heaven and Earth. It is He Who designed and constructed this world, with wisdom and intelligence, surely the Grandest Hotel of all.

The Great Move

I f you want to see a beautiful building, go to the new British library in London. Close to the famous Kings Cross Railway Station, in a building that dominates the skyline, rises the prestigious new library. Everything about the library has to be described in terms of superlative. The magnificent edifice, built at the cost of $868 million, is the largest publicly funded building constructed this century in Great Britain. The basements, which are the deepest in London, have about 200 miles of shelving for 12 million books. The library is staffed by no less than 1000 individuals. It houses the most important library collection in the world. Among its treasures are the world's earliest dated printed book (The Diamond Sutra — 868), The Magna Carta (1215), and Shakespeare's first Folio of 1623. The library houses over 150 million separate items, and on each working day, some 8000 items are added to the collection. Imagine having to find space on your bookshelf for 3 million separate items each year!

And think of the move. Until recently, all the British library's treasures were housed in 11 buildings scattered throughout London. All the millions of items, spanning three millennia, and including treasures of books and manuscripts, maps, stamps and photographs, had to be handled with the utmost care in the greatest move of books in history. A move of such magnitude cannot be undertaken overnight. Just contemplating the organization involved is awesome. The great move began at 9:30 a.m. Monday, December 2, 1996, and was completed in June of 1999. Two years, six months, and 14 days. That's some move!

But nothing compared to that which you are about to read. Answer a simple question. How does an acorn know it has to grow into an oak tree and not into a sunflower? How does a chicken egg know it has to grow into a chicken and not into a duck? Even more, how does the egg know how to grow into a chicken? From where does it receive the information? In the book *Not by Chance* by Lee M. Spetner Ph.D. (Jewish Heritage & Roots Library, October 1996) the answers are given with lucidity and authority. About 40 years ago, biologists began to learn how information plays its role in living organisms. They discovered the location of the information in the organism that tells it how to function and how to grow, how to live and how to reproduce. The information is in the seed as well as in the plant; it is in the egg as well as in the chicken.

Single cells are the smallest and simplest forms of living things that can reproduce themselves. Bacteria and yeast are examples of living cells. The bacterial cells are so small that a trillion of them could fit into a teaspoon. Yet it takes a lot of information to define a bacterium, and all of it is tucked

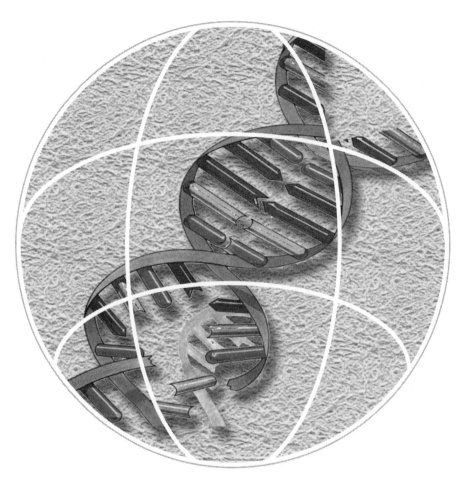

The splitting of a cell

into only a small fraction of the cell's tiny volume. The information in a cell plays a role much like that played by information in a factory. The production file in a factory contains a set of instructions that tell what each worker has to do at each stage. The production file is information carried by printed symbols; the developmental instructions in the cell are information carried by molecular symbols.

Most of the information in the cell is found on small bodies called *chromosomes*. In cells that have a nucleus (which includes all organisms except bacteria), the chromosomes are to be found in the cell's nucleus. The part of the chromosome that carries the information is the famous DNA molecule (*deoxyribonucleic acid*). All the DNA in all the chromosomes of a cell is called the *genome,* and the information is called *genetic information.* The chromosomes of some organisms may have much more DNA than are in the chromosomes of others, although the amount of DNA does not necessarily dictate the complexity of the organism. Although humans have 30 times the DNA of some insects, there are insects that have more than double the DNA of humans.

Amazingly, the DNA in the rod cells of the human eye contain all the information needed to produce a complete child! The DNA in an ear cell could theoretically construct a foot. Every cell contains in its DNA bank the complete dossier of information needed to construct the whole person. The reason the eye cell does not develop into anything but an eye cell is because large sections of the DNA template are blocked out. Only the relevant sections of the DNA are activated.

DNA can be compared to an architect whose job is to draw up the grand design for living. But it hands the work of building over to contractors — RNA (or *ribonucleic acid*). In the form of molecules, all information is "printed" on the interlocking spirals of DNA. "Messenger" RNA snuggles up to DNA spirals, and receives a blueprint of what is wanted. It then passes the word along to another form of RNA, "transfer" RNA. And the latter starts to work according to instructions — most likely building on the hundreds of proteins in the body. Just to have some idea of the cell's capability — the cells manufacture upward of 600 enzymes. On orders from the RNA, these master chemists instantly and effortlessly synthesize proteins — taking protein from a piece of fish, breaking it down into its components, and rearranging the amino acids to make the human protein needed for, say, your thumbnail. Enzymes in the cell also build bafflingly complex antibodies, and perform many tasks beyond the capabilities of the world's most gifted chemists.

The genome (all the DNA in the chromosomes) holds a mighty amount of information. The genome of the bacterium, for example, is a string of a few million symbols. The genome of a mammal has from two to four billion symbols. Lee Spetner has calculated that if you were to print those symbols in a book in ordinary type, the book for a bacterium would have about a thousand pages. The symbols for a mammal would fill 2,000 volumes, enough to take up a library shelf the length of two football fields! And all this information is in the tiny chromosomes of each and every cell, some 50 billion billion cells in all.

In the normal development of any living entity, two important functions must take place. The first is that beginning from a single cell, multiplication and replication must take place until the finished product is complete. And then, since no cell lasts forever, it must replace itself. The cellular division that initially forms life continues throughout life. Each second, millions of cells cease their vital functions — and millions more are born, by the process of old cells pulling apart, each to make two new ones — exact duplicates. Fat cells, largely storage bins, reproduce slowly, but skin cells reproduce every 10 hours. (One notable exception to this constant replacement is the brain. The moment we were born, we were in possession of the maximum number of brain cells we would ever have. Worn-out damaged cells are never replaced. But fear not, for the initial surplus was so great that we will scarcely notice the loss.)

It is in comparison to the replication of the cell that the great move of the British library appears puny. For in a very short space of time, all the vast amount of information contained in the chromosomes has to be duplicated, and accurately. It is simple enough to state that before the cell starts to divide, each chromosome produces an exact copy of itself. But concealed in that bland statement is the wonder of the DNA chemical-information library needing to produce a replica of itself.

The process is called *mitosis.* DNA has a double-helix shape like two intertwined corkscrews. In a vastly complex chemical process, the component strands of each double helix unwind, and regroup together forming a mirror image of itself. A new molecule of DNA is built up with exactly the same sequence of bases as the original partner. In this way the genetic code is preserved intact to be passed on with the chromosomes to the new cell. Where one chromosome existed previously, two sets now occupy the cell nucleus, each with their DNA information bank intact. The two sets then separate, each moving to opposite ends of the cell. The cell membrane (just .0000001 millimeter thick) grows through the middle of the cell, splitting it in two. So two complete new cells, each with an identical full set of genes, are formed from one parent cell. If not for mitosis, there could be no life. Unlike the British Library, this is not just a transfer of information, but a replication of it. It all happens, not in three years, but in seconds. Not once, but trillions of times.

A human being is a multicellular being. Each cell has its job and helps in its own way to promote the well-being of the whole organism. The cells cooperate with each other, enabling the organism as a whole to function efficiently. The ability of the cell to read its DNA information bank and know how to perform its allotted task, and its ability to perform the mind-boggling task of replicating itself, enable life to proceed. These twin functions must have been present from the beginning to allow life to exist. Together they provide the most eloquent testimony possible of the Great Intelligence that planned it, created it, and constantly gives it His blessing for continuity.

A Piece of Gefilte Fish

here's nothing like a trick question to keep people awake. Ask on which side of the king's gates Mordechai lit his Chanukah menorah, and you'll get everyone thinking. Pose the problem of how the *Kohanim* in the *Beis HaMikdash* were able to wash their hands and feet during the "Nine Days," and everyone will sit up and take notice. A similar query was recently heard. The whole world has heard of the *gefilte fish*, a rare species of fish found in *heimishe* oceans. The enquiry was how the gefilte fish manages to swim through the ocean and keep the piece of carrot on its head.

The question is really ridiculous because it is well known that the gefilte fish only has the piece of carrot added on its head after it has been caught.

A question of equal importance was asked by thinking people throughout the ages. Would it be possible for a ship to sail underwater? The military advantages in being able to move through the water undetected and attack enemy boats from below were obvious enough to occupy many great minds. The problems, however, were equally great. How to provide for propulsion, for fresh air, and how do you know where you are going? The acknowledged first submarine was built by a Dutchman called Cornelius Drebbel in the 1620s. He built a wooden rowboat, covered it with greased leather, with oars sticking through leather flaps, and submerged it in the River Thames in England. Great idea in theory, but the water poured through the flaps when it dived. A great step forward in design was made by the American engineer David Bushnell, whose "Turtle" dived and surfaced in 1776 by filling ballast tanks with water, then emptying them. Further progress. The first submarine to sink a ship was used by the Confederates in the American Civil War. In 1861 they rammed an enemy ship with an explosive charge mounted on the end of a wooden pole. Primitive, but effective. Their metal submarine was propelled by a propeller turned by hand-cranks! Today the submarine is one of the most important ships of the modern navy. It is nuclear powered, with the nuclear reactor working all the time, heating steam for a turbine. The submarine emits no fumes, and only needs to return to base once every two years for refueling, or whenever the crew run out of white shirts, whichever is sooner.

Hear another question. No human being wishing to remain healthy and well should try to remain underwater for longer than one minute. The supermodern submarine can manage only as long as its air supply lasts. How then does the fish (both gefilte and other species) manage to remain underwater forever? All animals, from eagles to fish, need oxygen in order to survive. On land, oxygen is found in the

How does it keep the piece of carrot on its head?

air breathed into the lungs. Water contains oxygen too, in a dissolved form. Fish "breathe" in the water using a specialized invention called gills. Oxygen passes from the water through the thin gill membranes into the fish's blood, and is then pumped around the body. It sounds simple, but like everything in the created world, it is anything but. It relies on a system in the gills called the counter-current flow, by which water is pumped past the gills in the opposite direction to the blood flowing in the gills. This arrangement ensures that the oxygen and carbon dioxide concentrations in the blood never reach equilibrium, for if it did, the vital exchange of carbon dioxide for oxygen could not occur.

It is vital that a constant flow of water is maintained over the gills to allow diffusion (the gas exchange — you take my carbon dioxide, and give me your oxygen) to take place. Water needs to be taken in, and an outlet is required to allow the deoxygenated water to escape. Fortunately, fish have been supplied with a mouth at the front, and gill flaps (*operculum*) at the side. Fish use pumping actions of the floor of the mouth, combined with rhythmic opening and closing of the operculum, to send a steady stream of water over the gills. A mouthful of water is taken in at the front, while the gill cover shuts flat to prevent water escaping past it. The fish then closes its mouth and pressurizes the water within. This flows past the gills, where the life-giving diffusion takes place, and pushes open the flaplike gill covers on the way out. Just like your own lungs, gills are covered in a thin layer of cells less than 5 microns thick, and networks of fine capillaries pass close to this surface. What lungs do with air, gills perform with water. The gills of a large, active fish — such as a tuna — must extract plentiful oxygen from the water to power the great muscular activity. Under each gill cover are four gills, each supported by a V-shaped bony arch. There is a double row of gill filaments on each arch, and each filament is made of many leaflike folds called *lamellae*. This gives a large surface area for absorbing oxygen — up to 10 times the area of the fish's body.

A submarine that fails to close its conning tower when it dives is in for a watery shock. Why does it not have an automatic cover? Its watery friends do! Whales and dolphins rise to the surface from time to time to breathe out a spurt of water vapor and air, and gulp in fresh air through a blowhole on the top of their head. Powerful muscles close the hole while they are diving. No one needs to tell them; the system is automatic. Early submarines had no air-storage facilities — and carbon dioxide breathed out by the crew became a major problem if the craft was forced to stay submerged for long periods. Pity they could not learn from the whales. There is a special pigment called *myoglobin* which is used in the muscles to store oxygen, releasing it only at very low oxygen levels. Seals and other diving mammals, which must go for a relatively long time without breathing, have been blessed with particularly large amounts of myoglobin, allowing them to remain down below in happiness and good health. Myoglobin does not happen by accident!

How does the captain of a submerged submarine know what is happening in the water around him? Perhaps at that very moment an enemy submarine is charging towards him! His periscope is fine above the surface, but useless down below. Perhaps he should ask a hapless member of his crew (wearing his raincoat) to pop out of the conning tower and have a quick look round? No problem for the fish. Water is an excellent carrier of sound vibrations. Fish can sense these vibrations by means of a wonderful invention. It is called a *lateral line*, that runs along each side of the fish, under the skin. The sound vibrations pass into the canal via tiny pores in the skin, and agitate tiny lumps of jelly there. Vibration-sensitive hairs are embedded in the mass of jelly, and these microscopic hairs convert the vibrations into electrical impulses which travel along sensory nerves to the fish's brain, where the brain interprets the impulses and takes appropriate action. There are some fish, sharks for example, that can detect prey not only by scent through their nostrils, not only by vision through their large eyes, but with electricity-detecting organs located around its nose. Indeed, if you are swimming at the beach, and someone mentions that the great white shark (sharks never stop growing new teeth, triangular in shape with sharp tips and serrated edges) has been spotted in the vicinity, it might be advisable to choose that moment to leave the water ... you never know how much electricity you are producing! Please note. Electricity-detecting organs do not happen by themselves. Neither you or I, let alone submarines, have this supersophisticated system, much as we would like them.

What modern submarines do have is sonar equipment. This invention sends out and receives sonar beams. The sonar (short for "sound navigation and ranging") system sends out a sound beam which spreads until it detects an object. The beam then echoes back, and the returning waves are converted into electrical impulses that form an image on a screen. It is indeed a fantastic invention — thought of by a French inventor in 1918 — but the playful dolphins have possessed it since they were created. Dolphins produce trains of clicks which sound like a door creaking, not through their mouth, but in nasal tubes just beneath their blowhole. A dolphin has a waxy bulge in the forehead which is thought to be a lens to focus the sounds it produces. The sounds travel through the water, meet another object, perhaps a fish, and bounce back. The echoes are heard through an inner ear, located where the lower jaw meets the skull. This ability to locate objects through echos (called echo-location) is an incredibly precise sense. Blindfolded, dolphins can still find objects, or tell between two balls of slightly different size. Not only that. It is thought that the high-pitched sounds that they produce also stuns fish, so that the dolphin can make an easy catch. Copy that one, submarine!

Ever wondered how a submarine dives? Perhaps by thinking about it? Valves are opened to let sea water into ballast tanks, increasing the submarine's weight. To surface, compressed air is blown into the tanks, to expel the water; just like fish. Many bony fish have a swim bladder (a thin-walled air sac) between the gut and the spine. Changes in the air pressure within the swim bladder, produced by air entering the bladder from the gut or surrounding capillaries, help the fish maintain buoyancy at different water depths.

Down beneath the sea, the humble fish swim with the ultramodern submarine. We know how much thought and intelligence has been invested in the pride of the world's navies. It helps give us a small indication of the vast intelligence that lies inherent in the design and production of all fish. Is it surprising then that on *Shabbos kodesh* we take a small sample — gefilte fish — and offer our grateful testimony to the One Who created it all?

Black Gold

The rising sun peeped over the horizon, illuminated the inside of Yosef's hut, and woke him up. He sighed. The night had been too short, and the very thought of the coming day made him feel weary and tired. He would have to plow the top field, a back-breaking job which involved harnessing his two oxen to a rough wooden plow and guiding its jolting progress through the unyielding soil. Life for Yosef and his family was not easy. If the crops failed or the animals died, there was no hope of importing any from abroad. Their tattered clothes, usually homemade, offered little protection against the bitter cold, hail, rain, snow and high winds that characterized Northern Europe. Their hut, with its thatched roof, was usually damp, and the chilling cold penetrated to the furthest recesses of every crack. There is no doubt about it, life 1000 years ago was tough; the workload of the ordinary man was harsh and relentless.

Try and imagine yourself talking to Yosef, and describing a day in your life. (And imagine that "Yourself" is as humble a person as you could find.) Your house is built from brick, and glass fills the window frames. When your electric alarm clock awakes you in the morning, the house has already been heated by central heating, preset by the timer and thermostat. Dressing means putting on the clothes bought in a large department store, which in turn have been imported from a host of countries from around the globe. After returning from *davening* (in your private automobile — a self-propelling horseless carriage constructed from metal, glass, rubber and plastic, and fueled by gas), you prepare your breakfast. Neither the bread nor the butter, the cereal nor the sugar, the coffee nor the water — nor any of the utensils that you use to consume them — have been grown or produced by yourself. Almost everything that you eat is imported from another country. You tell him of the carpets on your floor (which cover the floorboards, which cover the joists, which cover the foundations); your cabinet which maintains a winterlike temperature even in the hottest summer days; your precious piece of plastic (plastic?), which, just by holding in your hand, enables you to talk to anyone in the world; and the white metal box that achieves the greatest wonder of all. You insert all your dirty garments, close the lid, and in less than one hour, all the garments can be removed, absolutely clean! Be honest. Would he believe you? Even fairy stories of a thousand years ago would not have dreamed of such wonders. And you consider yourself hard up?

It would be hard, if not impossible, for us to return to the life of one millennium ago. Would you have any idea how to light a fire without matches? Could you produce a loaf of

Vital oil from under the ocean. Which great Intelligence put it there in the first place?

bread from your back yard? Even if you were fortunate enough to be the proud owner of some sheep would you have the know-how to produce a Shabbos suit from the sheep's back, or a *shtreimel* from a fox's tail? Given the choice between primitive and harsh living conditions of a thousand years ago, and the relative affluence enjoyed by Mr. Average today, most people would opt for the latter. That being the case, it is worth bearing in mind that were it not for one single substance, all the modern inventions mentioned above would either not exist, or even if they existed, would be inoperable. That substance is so fundamental that modern life would be impossible without it. The most amazing thing is that this substance is not manmade, nor is it manufactured. It is something that was placed into the earth at the time of Creation, and for thousands of years, either no one knew of its existence, or even if they did, had no idea of its potential. What is it?

Oil. Like so many things in our world, oil is a substance which we take completely for granted. We think of it fleetingly when we fill up the tank with gas, and read the notice "Have you checked your oil level?" In much the same way that many people imagine that electricity is produced "somehow" inside wall sockets, an equal number (probably the same people) are convinced that oil is produced inside the gas pump. Not quite. In its natural form, oil is a thick black or dark brown liquid, which is found underground in many parts of the world. This natural substance is called crude oil, and contains two main elements — hydrogen and carbon. Even though oil has been used for about 2000 years (in ancient China, oil was used in simple lamps, while the native Americans used it as a medicine. Crude oil sometimes occurred as a black, sticky substance called pitch, and was used as a waterproof coating), but it is only since the 19th century that it has become the most important of all the world's minerals.

We could not imagine a world without oil. Oil provides fuel for transport (ship, car, plane, train — just about everything except the pogo stick), fuel for cooking; and heats our homes. It generates electricity, and is essential for heat processes in industry. Oil is so valuable to us that it is sometimes called "black gold." Without oil, our modern world would grind to a halt. Our industries would stop working, and all machines would cease functioning in a screaming cacophony of grinding metal. All machines need lubricants to allow them to operate smoothly. In the same way that fluid between your joints allows them to move without painfully rubbing together, similarly lubricants work by reducing the friction between two surfaces that are rubbing against each other.

Thousands of different types of lubricants are made from crude oil, from the very thinnest of oil for watches to the thickest of grease for heavy machinery. The uses of oil are almost endless. Think of an oil refinery. Hissing pipes, steaming towers, sprawling tanks and waiting tankers are all part of the process that heats up the crude oil, turning it first into vapor, and then passing it into the refining towers where it separates into various parts. Bitumen is used to pave the tough road surface; heavy fuel oil is burned in ship engines; diesel oil ignites trains and trucks; kerosene is used for aircraft fuel; and thinner oil provides the gas for your car.

And don't forget plastic! Many types of plastics are made from oil. Look around your home and count them. Almost any item in the home could be made from plastic, from buckets to toothbrushes, baths, bowls, toys, dishes, telephones, computers, tablecloths, cutlery and — most important of all — false teeth. The paint that brightens up your house is made from plastic solvents that come from oil; any nylon, terylene or acrylic garments that you possess are also derivatives of oil. Approximately 10 percent of the world's crude oil is now made into petrochemicals, which are made into a wide range of materials. Think of detergents for washing up, glycerine for drugs solvents for paint and glue, chemicals for agriculture, synthetic rubber for car tires and hard-wearing soles for shoes, glycol for antifreeze, and the plastic duck that floats in your bath — each and every one is derived from the black sticky substance that lies beneath the earth's surface.

Think of the following. A well-run store will keep a good stock of the items that its customers require — and the quantity of the goods will be commensurate with the demand. A hardware store will keep a large quantity and a full variety of screws, because many people need screws; but since the demand for horseshoes for left-footed camels is significantly lower, the store's left-footed horseshoe department will probably be quite small. This world has been created with design, intent, and intelligence. Certain items are required in greater quantity than others. Consequently, the supply is more abundant. Every creature needs oxygen — so the supply of oxygen is limitless and free. We all need water in plentiful supply — so rain falls everywhere, it is free, and it can be collected. The use that we have for gold is very limited — consequently its supply is limited. In the 20th century, everyone needs oil. Not surprisingly, oil is found on every continent except Antarctica. New supplies of oil are still being found all over the world. China now produces large amounts of oil, and Egypt and Thailand have recently become oil producers. Oil companies are always looking for new sources of oil, and new reserves are being found in out-of-the-way places such as the North Sea and Alaska. Perhaps you'll find some in your own back yard.

This world is a planned place. It is neither haphazard nor accidental. The Creator knew that there would be an industrial revolution, and the world would require fuel. That fuel had to be placed into position, ready for discovery and use. The vast quantity of oil to be found underground is a clear indication that the Creator knew of the multifaceted need for this wonder-substance. For hundreds of years, it lay there patiently, undiscovered and unneeded. Whoever did know of its existence had no idea of its use. Its time had not come. When it was needed, it was discovered. The more it is needed, the more its sources will be discovered. Black it might be, but as valuable as gold it most certainly is. Its greatest value? To provide us with a remarkable example of a world created with unmistakable design.

Accurate Memories

Everyone loves a *chasunah;* and all for different reasons. The happy *chasan* and *kallah* and their close family naturally have their own private joy. For others, usually young, the wedding affords them the opportunity to fling themselves around the hall with unmitigated abandon in accompaniment to the raucous music, thus releasing much pent-up energy. Others still think of a wedding purely in terms of food. They don't eat for two days before the big event in order to be able to arrive at the *simchah* with an unabashed and unabated appetite, and proceed to devour the tastefully prepared foods as if the seven years of hunger were about to begin. For these good folks, the actual *chupah* is an irrelevance, and the dancing during the meal an irritation. Once upon a time, the wedding was performed, photographs were taken, and that was that. Nothing tangible remained of the great day except happy memories, a cluster of invoices, and of course, the *bayis ne'eman* itself.

Not any more! We have arrived at the age of the camcorder. A camcorder, for the benefit of the uninitiated, is a combination of an electronic camera and video recorder in one package. It is light and compact, held in one hand, and can record any event onto a video film, which can later be played back. This great "blessing" to mankind was introduced into the market by Sony in 1982, and since then it has taken over many people's lives. There are three million camcorders in Great Britain alone, and it is impossible to visit any famous location without being berated for wandering into someone's precious recording. (Some take it even further. Police were called to a traffic accident on the Santa Monica Freeway near Los Angeles, and found one of the drivers involved recording their arrival on his camcorder. To their amazement, he asked them to go back and "arrive" again, this time with full lights and sirens!) Go to any *chasunah* and there is a good chance that some enthusiast will be recording the event for posterity on his cool camcorder. For every tear of happiness that is shed by the nearest and dearest, at least one film will be completed by the camcorder fraternity. It is always a source of bewilderment to the more curious among us as to where the *baalei simchah*, or anyone else for that matter, will watch the finished product, since our *gedolim* have fiercely denounced the possession of a VCR (video cassette recorder). Be that as it may, the camcorder seems here to stay.

Prejudice apart, it really is a marvelous machine. It records all sights and sounds straight onto a cassette, it has a playback feature, together with automatic focus, automatic aperture opening, and high-speed shutter. It comes complete with zoom lens and electronic viewfinder. Even your most

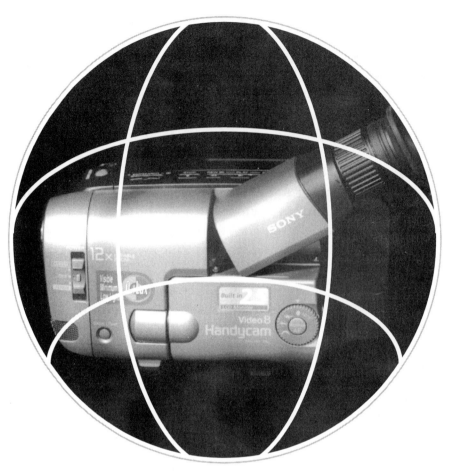

Ultrasophisticated camcorder – nearly as good as the real thing.

sophisticated single-shot conventional camera looks positively archaic by comparison. But wait — when Shlomo Hamelech told us that there is nothing new under the sun, he was absolutely right. This ultimate sophisticated Japanese import, the last word in advanced technology, is not new at all. Because reading these very lines at the front of your face are two of the smartest, complex, efficient camcorders you have ever seen!

Just study the matter superficially, and let us return to the wedding. Everyone present is watching the event. With what? His very own two cameras. Each camera works independently, focuses automatically, and has an automatic iris to control the entry of light into the aperture. Both cameras come protected by an overhanging rocky forehead, fencelike eyelashes, neat-fitting eyelid covers, and an automatic washing-cleansing facility, complete with an in-house production factory and drainage system. An additional safety feature ensures that should any object (such as a fist or a stone) be thrown towards your twin cameras, your brain (main computer) has been programmed to instruct your arm to fly up and block the object, while the same instinct will make you lower your head behind the protective arm. Everything is seen in full color, and no extra lighting is necessary. You will notice that after the guests have looked at something with their twin eye-cameras, they do not run to the chemist to develop that which they have seen. It is all done automatically, and the finished product is available and visible instantaneously.

Playback facility? No problem at all. Whatever you see enters your memory. Should you desire a re-view, just close your eyes and think of that which you have seen, and there it will be. Of all the millions of memories stored in your memory-collecting bank, just that very memory that you request can be recalled instantly. That is just a superficial view. Now look at some of the advantages that your twin-camera eyes have over the camcorder. What does Mr. Camcorder enthusiast do when the film in his cassette runs out in the middle of the last *berachah*? What does he do if he accidentally uncovers the batteries and all the electricity runs out, leaving his marvelous machine as flat as a day-old pancake? Your eyes require neither film nor batteries. Your sight will not run out, and never once will you have to check the battery level of your eyes. The camcorder can only record light waves and sound waves. It will give you an audio-visual record of the grand event. Your twin-camera eyes will not only record every single detail, and your sensitive ears every sound, but you will also receive an aroma memory in which the multiscented fragrances of the day will be forever etched in your memory, together with all the emotions that each one evoked. Try putting that in your camcorder!

You must have heard about the man, who at the airport departure lounge, said to his wife, "I wish we could have brought along the grand piano!" His wife looked at him with some surprise, and asked why — "Because our tickets are on top of it!" murmured the husband sheepishly. Never mind plane tickets, what would happen if you discovered that you had left the camcorder at home when you arrived at the big event? That disaster is something that can never happen with your twin cameras. With your two eyes firmly fixed (each one attached by six slim muscles) in your head, it's hard to forget them.

If only a superficial observation of our own twin cameras puts the camcorders firmly in the shade, imagine what a closer look will do. Try a small experiment. Look at a small object, such as the tip of a pen, about a foot away. Cover one eye, then the other, as you study it. Each view is different, because each eye looks at the object from a different angle. See how the lines of the object's edges and the shapes of its surfaces alter slightly between the two views. The brain takes these two views and combines them into one image. The different angles and surfaces in this combined three-dimensional image provide us with information about how far away the object is. With just one eye it is much harder to judge distances.

Eyes work by changing light energy into the electrical energy of nerve impulses. Light rays behave like waves; the difference between pulses of energy is the wavelength. Different wavelengths produce different colors of light. The transformation from light to electricity is carried out by special cells containing colored pigments — chemicals that absorb certain colors of light. The light energy they absorb causes chemical changes in the pigments releasing some of the energy. This energy is turned into electrical energy and passed along the nerve cells to the brain. Sounds complicated, doesn't it? Well, it is. But how efficient! The human eye contains about 130 million rods and cones (light-receiving stations) in the retina at the back of the eye, and can distinguish more than 10 million different colors — more colors than any machine that is used to analyze light.

Everything that we take for granted is a wonder almost beyond description. The eye is held in position and moved by external muscles. Someone put them there! The spherical eyeball is filled with vitreous humor, a clear jelly that provides the pressure to keep the eye in shape. This fluid contains dissolved oxygen and supplies the lens and the cornea (the window at the front of the eye that partly focuses light rays and is so transparent that you can hardly see it when looking at your eye in the mirror), which themselves do not have blood vessels, with oxygen and nutrients. The lens, which has the remarkable ability to alter its shape in order to focus light rays from objects at different distances, has to remain suspended just behind the pupil to maintain its flexibility. How do you get yourself suspended? Special suspensory ligaments, which themselves are attached to muscles, keep the lens perfectly balanced and positioned. The cornea, the window at the front of the eye, must be kept moist to prevent it from drying out and desiccating. Not surprisingly, just made to order, you have another transparent skin, the conjuctiva, which forms a moist covering over the cornea.

Our two eyes provide an incredibly detailed, constantly updated, three-dimensional color view of the world. The eye is intricate and sophisticated beyond belief; it is a most wonderful machine. The Sony camcorder gives us some framework (primitive and limited though it is!) with which to compare the eye. Thank you, Mr. Sony, for your assistance, and thank You, Hashem *Yisbarach*, for those brilliant windows to the world — our very own eyes.

The Fantastic Time Machine

Have you ever had the following nightmare? You've been invited to give a *shiur* (usually, if it's a dream, the audience is prestigious and vast). You walk up to the podium, and wait for silence. The audience coughs a little, the chatter diminishes, and in the silence of eager anticipation, they wait for you to begin. Everyone is keenly anticipating your words of wisdom, and you have this great awareness of the importance of this moment. Time has frozen — never before have so many people focused their full attention directly on you — this is the moment. Suddenly, as you begin with your opening words, "*Rashei Yeshivah, chashever Rabbanim,* good friends, *Morei v'Rabbosai ...*" you realize that you haven't the foggiest idea what you are going to say. It's a nightmare, remember! You have a *Chumash* in front of you. Desperately you say, "*Es shteiht in passuk, the Torah tells us ...*" and, panic stricken, fumble through the pages, seeking inspiration. Nothing. The *pessukim* are unfamiliar, pages are missing, you notice the *Chumash* is upside down, the *Chumash* turns into a *siddur...* what a nightmare! In the meantime, the audience becomes impatient, suggestions are called out, the moment of anticipation is lost. As you continue your hopeless search for something to say, people drift out of the hall, and, mouth dry, you wake up!

It might be a nightmare, but all too often it's true. The *maggid shiur,* who has his listeners in the palm of his hand, looks in his *sefer* for a reference, can't find it, spends precious minutes humming and hawing while flipping through the pages, and by the time he finds it, the rapt attention is lost, possibly never to be regained. The speaker who begins a moment too soon, just before that magical moment of silence, might have lost the opportunity to capture the audience. The piano accompanist who commences the musical accompaniment just one half-second too late, ruins the performance. The producer of a show, who keeps his audience waiting too long between scenes, risks losing their good will. The caterer, who takes just a little too long to bring each course, risks losing his clientele. A car engine where the timing is faulty, so that the spark from the plug is fired just before the fuel is introduced in the combustion chamber, will not work. It may be just a fraction of a second out of sync, in matters of timing that could be the difference between success and failure. The punch line of a joke, told a second too early, will fall flat. Timing is all important.

Nowhere is timing more important than your very own pump that never tires. A little insight into a mighty organ can only serve to heighten one's appreciation of the Creator. The heart is a muscular pump which beats nonstop for —

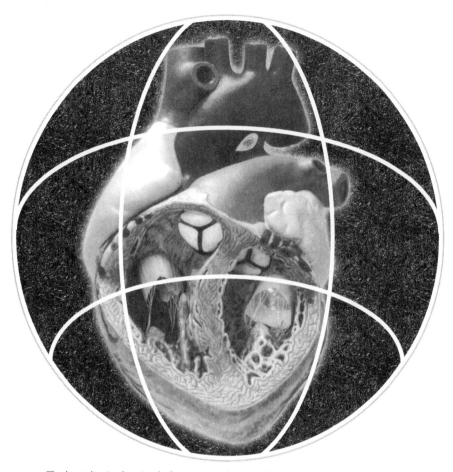

The heart begins beating before you are born and keeps you going for 120 years.

and so we wish everyone — 120 years. It repairs and lubricates itself, and is capable of an almost instant variation of blood output from 1 to 5 gallons a minute. The amount of work performed by the heart is astonishing. It is equivalent to a man lifting a 14-pound weight to a height of 5 feet once each second. After lifting the weight a few dozen times, the brave man would probably be exhausted. But the heart goes on pumping, day after day, year after year — for a lifetime.

The heart's task is to pump blood to each and every part of the body. When you bear in mind that the blood vessels form an immense branching network, with a total length in

each single person of over 60,000 miles, you begin to understand what a fantastic machine we are dealing with. Its
efficiency is almost beyond belief. The shortest return trip
that blood makes from the heart — to the heart's own muscle — takes only a few seconds. The longest, to the toes, takes
not too much longer. Centrally situated in the middle of the
chest (slightly more to the left side than the right) your marvelous pump weighs only about 14 ounces, and is the size of
a man's fist. (Having said that, people born with extra-large
hearts often make excellent athletes. There was once a run-
ner named Paavo Nurmi, who won nine Olympic gold medals,
whose heart was three times larger than normal! So now you
know!) The heart is surrounded and protected by a membrane called the *pericardium,* and the whole brilliantly
designed machine is further protected by the rib cage.

The heart is really two pumps lying side by side, and each
has both an upper and a lower chamber. There is no direct
connection between the two sides of the heart. Its layout resembles a two-story house with two rooms on each floor. The
only entrances are into the upstairs rooms, and the only ex-
its lead from the lower ones. On each side of the house there
is a downward-opening trap door which makes it possible to
move from upstairs to downstairs. It is impossible to move up
through the trap door, or to go from one side of the house to
the other.

Each of the four rooms has a clearly defined and highly
specialized job. And timing is all important. Blood, carrying
oxygen from the lungs, enters the top left chamber (*left atrium*). This chamber contracts, squeezing the blood through
the one-way valve into the lower left chamber (*left ventricle*). As the ventricle fills, the blood eddies, causing the flaps
of the valve to flutter upwards and close the passage. The
pressure beneath the valve shuts it tight. (Ever wondered
how you develop a valve? It has to work perfectly to work
at all, and without valves you have no machine. And without a machine ... sorry, Mr. Darwin, it seems you have a
slight problem!) A fraction of a second later, this chamber

contracts pumping the blood into the *main artery*, the *aorta*. This chamber is the most muscular of them all, for it is the contraction of this chamber which sends the blood on its 60,000-mile odyssey. This is not to say that each droplet of blood travels 60,000 miles in the course of one minute. It is estimated that if all the blood vessels in the body's transport system were laid end to end, the total length would be more than 60,000 miles. In reality, the blood vessels form an immense branching network. They fan out from the heart and eventually converge back there. The shortest return trip that blood makes — to the heart's own muscle — takes only a few seconds. The longest — to the toes — takes over a minute. The aorta branches into several large arteries, and again into many smaller arteries, until eventually they have divided into huge numbers of tiny *capillaries* that deliver blood directly to cells. There are so many capillaries that no part of your body — with a few exceptions like your teeth — is further from a capillary than the thickness of this paper!

Blood in the capillaries delivers oxygen and fuel to the cells and picks up waste products. It then starts the long trip back to the heart through a system of tubes called *veins*. Blood makes the entire trip from the heart to the furthest parts of the body and back to the heart again in about 65 seconds. Efficient? The returning blood enters the upper right-hand chamber of the heart (*right atrium*). The chamber contracts, sending the returning blood down into the lower right-hand chamber (*right ventricle*). A fraction of a second later, the filled chamber contracts, squeezing the blood to the lungs (by way of the *pulmonary artery*) to empty out its load of unwanted carbon dioxide, and take on fresh supplies of oxygen. You understand why there has to be a fractional delay between the contraction of the lower chambers and the upper chambers. There would be little purpose in the ventricles contracting if the blood has not yet arrived from the upper chambers. Hence the crucial — yet vitally important — timing.

Two special features make the heart incredibly versatile and hard working. The first is the muscle in the heart's walls. It is called *cardiac muscle,* and, unlike normal muscle, it never tires. The second is the heart's ability to change its pumping speed and its force to match the body's needs. Nerve signals from the brain, and hormones from the blood, all help to control these changes. Add to this the ability to maintain perfect timing, and you begin to appreciate the intelligence behind its design and construction.

The power which causes the chambers to contract and perform their vital pumping action is fired by the inherent electrical power contained in the heart muscles themselves. This is the all-important *heartbeat,* medically known as the *cardiac impulse.* However, without an internal control, the rate of the heartbeats, about 40 per minute, would be insufficient to meet the demands made by the extensive range of the body's activities. Enter the *pacemaker!* This pacemaker, issued free with each heart, is composed of two masses of nerve tissue, called *nodes,* and it overrides the cardiac impulse and speeds up the heartbeat to an average of about 70 per minute. The electrical impulse begins in a region of the right atrium (upper chamber), and spreads out into the walls of the atria causing their contraction. But wait — if the contraction would continue down into the ventricles, they would contract too early, for they wouldn't yet have filled with blood! Don't worry, it has all been thought of. The cardiac impulse is prevented from spreading directly to the ventricles by specially designed nonconductive material, called the *fibrous ring.* Instead it is picked up by another node, and from here it is transferred to the ventricles by special circuitry, causing the lower chambers to contract a fraction of a second later, at precisely the right time.

It is doubtful whether you will find another machine anywhere in the world where the need for precise timing is so crucial.

It is dubious also whether anywhere in the world you will find a machine that requires such a degree of complexity and sophistication in its construction, yet works so efficiently. It is in place, beating away, even before you are born, and it keeps you going, beating strongly, for 120 years. A matchbox doesn't make itself; how much more so this 14-ounce super-sophisticated lifesaver. "A word in its right time is a good thing." Thank You, *Hashem Yisbarach*, for Your great gift and superb machinery.

Hair Raising

imes have changed. Once upon a time, when someone became engaged, or had a baby, you went to them, extended the right hand, and wished Mazel Tov. If you knew them well, and felt particularly happy at their good fortune, you shook the hand with extra vigor and wished them "A very big (or a *groisse groisse*) Mazel Tov." They got the message, and were happy enough. That was in the old days. Then, some enterprising individual discovered helium (a gas lighter than air) and, as part of the inflationary process, began filling balloons with this gas. On the balloons were written such inspiring words as "It's a boy!" (in case the parents were unaware), or "Well done" (as if becoming engaged was a heroic achievement, which, on second thoughts, it may well be!). Now, no *simchah* is complete without a spectrum of balloons firmly fastened to the carriage handle or the back of the *kallah's* chair.

That much is now history. The big question is: How do you attach a piece of string to an inflated balloon? How about threading the string through a large needle, and inserting the needle into the balloon in order to pull it through to the other side? Would it work? Let us say that you had a much larger balloon, a hot-air balloon for example, and while you were attempting a round-the-world voyage, floating at 20,000 feet, you wished to erect a radio antenna at the apex of your beautiful balloon in order to receive congratulatory messages. Could you push the metal aerial, with its sharp metallic point, through the fabric of the balloon? In either case, please don't try it. It could be disastrous.

Why is it, then, that your very own body (particularly the skin) can remain both waterproof and airtight even though it is pierced many thousand of times over by individual hairs? How does it work? Another question. Why is that the hair on a person's head grows continually at the rate of approximately 5 inches a year (you will be fascinated to know that an Indian gentleman was reported to have a head of hair 26 feet in length) whereas the hair on your eyelashes and eyebrows grows to a very specific length, and then stops growing? Why is it that the eyelashes curl outwards and not (painful even to think of it) inwards? Why is it that no matter how full a man's beard, it will never grow on his forehead or on his lips? The answer to these and many similar questions provide an amazing insight into the wisdom that lies inherent in the very things that we most likely take for granted and consider simple.

There is nothing simple in the created world. Come, little hair, and tell your story. Imagine a factory. Like all factories, it has a production line, supply routes which bring in the raw materials, and of course, communication with other fac-

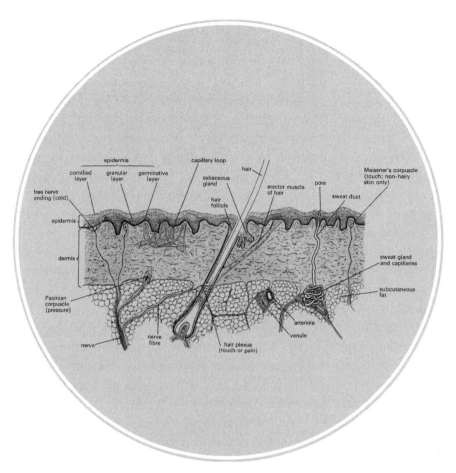

A section through skin

tories. Every single factory has to be maintained, serviced, and well planned if it is to function efficiently. There is no doubt that a single factory provides ample evidence of intelligent planning. What would you say about an industrial area which contains no less than 3 million factories? The trading estate is you, and the 3 million factories are the *follicle* — the name given to the tiny factory which produces and maintains an individual hair. A follicle is simply (not quite so simple!) a minute hair factory, an amazing and complex operation that operates 24 hours a day for up to seven years, and then shuts down for rest and repairs. After a rest period, the follicle will crank up and begin producing again.

It is an interesting fact that already three months before birth, you possessed all the hair follicles you will ever have. No new follicles appear after birth, so whether a person has a thick or thin growth of hair on his head is largely determined by hereditary factors. Scientists are amazed (to use their words) that anything as tiny as a follicle could produce something as intricate as a hair, and indeed a single hair is anything but simple. Each individual hair is made up almost entirely of protein (the same material as your nails), and consists of several layers. The outer layer has overlapping cells that resemble the shingles on a roof. That gives strength and protection. The middle layer contains fatter elongated cells which give bulk. Most hairs have a hollow core ("Blessed are You, Hashem, Who fashioned man with wisdom, and created within him many openings and many cavities..."). The base, or bulb, of each follicle is connected to blood vessels that supply nutrients to the hair. Each hair requires nutrition, and its vital sustenance is delivered to the doorstep. Sending out 3 million specialized food packages each day is no simple matter — ask any caterer! In addition, each follicle is connected to the nervous system, even though the hair itself contains no living matter. For this reason, if a hair is pulled out, pain is felt at the root; but cutting hair, even close to the skin, is painless. Just imagine that your hair did contain nerves — how could you ever brush your hair, or worse still, how could you ever cut it! In an intelligently planned system, nothing is without reason.

How strong is hair? Very strong. It has elasticity (under certain conditions it can be stretched to double its length), and an individual hair can support a three-ounce weight. Every hair follicle is serviced by one or more oil glands. This gland (called the *sebaceous gland*) gives the hair its flexibility and waterproof quality. Interestingly enough, the oily substance, called *sebum,* mingles with sweat and spreads over the skin, helping it to remain supple and water repellent. Place a drop of water on the palm of your hand, and it will remain intact. For that you can thank your "natural" oil reserves. (In fact, human skin is "showerproof" rather than fully waterproof. After a long soak in the bathtub, the sebum is washed away. Water can then enter the skin, making it appear soggy and wrinkled.)

Apart from the oil gland, every individual hair is attached to a tiny muscle, called an *erector muscle*. In furry animals, this tiny muscle is attached to the base of each hair. It can pull the hair base to make the hair stand on end. This happens when the animal wants to appear huge and fierce, when your friendly pussycat is not so friendly. It also happens when it is cold. Air becomes trapped between the erect hair, creating an air blanket to keep in body heat. Our hair is much smaller than that of animals, but it stands on end in exactly the same way when we are frightened ("the things children do makes your hair stand on end!") or when we are cold ("goose pimples").

If you have ever been to a busy airport, you will have seen how each terminal has many gates, at which each individual airplane is serviced by a fuel tanker, catering van, cleaning staff and the tough little truck that pushes it out to the runway. An airport is a vastly complex and coordinated operation, indicative of much thought and planning. Are your 3 million follicles, serviced and maintained by fuel tanks and muscles (all interconnected and joined to the central computer), any differently? What about the catering? At the base of each follicle sits a hair bulb drawing nutrients from the lower layer of skin, the *dermis*. In this bulb, a cone of tissue — the *papilla* and *matrix* — assembles the chemicals that will send up a hair.

All hair has color. What determines its particular shade? When a hair is still forming, it is impregnated with thousands of tiny packets of melanin pigments. Cells called *melanocytes* produce and blend only two basic "paints" to produce the exotic palette of different colors we see in human hair. One pigment tints our flowing locks deep black to the lightest brown. The other pigment turns the hair blond to golden brown or red. By varying the size, shape, illumination and density of the pigments, human hair becomes an assortment of colors. Many people are born with blond hair, but it slowly grows darker as the dark pigmentation becomes more active. As we pass our 20s, malanocyte production slows down. Emerging hairs, possessing only a tiny amount of their former pigment, begin to appear grey. When the melanocytes go completely dormant, hair grows out with no pigment at all, and is the natural color of hair protein — white. It is a fact that in centuries past, grey was a mark of sagacity. Everyone wanted to look old, for that was to appear wise. It is a telling indication of this generation's youth-loving culture that in the non-Jewish world, 40 percent of women and 8 percent of men dye their hair to conceal the grey. Great hope has been given to these people by recent research that shows that dormant melanocytes can be triggered to paint the hair once again with natural hues, in some cases restoring its original color. What a relief!

Iyov said it all. "From my flesh I perceive Hashem" (*Job* 9:26). He could well have been looking at a single hair. It's all there. Different function, different hair. It's all part of the plan. Eyelashes are curved and spiky — their duty is defense. Hair on the lips, the soles of the feet or on the palms of our hands would be a considerable source of irritation; thus, of the total surface of the body, these are the only areas to have none. And the balloon question? How can hair grow through the skin without puncturing it? Why, it's just one of the marvels of a machine whose wonder and complexity almost defies comprehension. When you have an instrument manufactured by a Creator of unlimited wisdom, the wonders are limitless. Just take a look and see!

Blowing in the Wind

Do you keep your eye on current fashions? If so, you will no doubt have noticed that men's hats have changed radically. Around 30 years ago, they were small, narrow-brimmed snappy things. The fact that many peacocks were running around half bald demonstrated the popularity of feathers in men's hats. Turn the clock forward, and you will notice, firstly, that the feathers have returned to their nests, and secondly, you get an awful lot of hat for your money. Brims have broadened, crowns have heightened, and the makers' names feature prominently on the outside of their products. (Why any consumer should agree to advertise the name of their hat manufacturer without a reduction in price is one of the mysteries of modern life!) Some hats are so high that they should be fitted with a red light on top to warn off low-flying aircraft! Smart they may look, snazzy they may feel, but they are not easy to wear on a windy day. An ultra-broad brim may have an additional use as a permanent umbrella, but as a windbreak they are fatal. We all like to maintain our dignity but that is not so easy while you are chasing your airborne hat along the road during a storm, one hand clutching your *yarmulka* for dear life, the other hand desperately outstretched to grab the hat before it flies into orbit.

In fact, many things are difficult to do on a windy day. One imagines that the weather a *kallah* most fears for her outdoor wedding is a howling storm. If, on a windy day, you ever see a *chupah* flying through the air with four hapless men suspended at each corner, you'll know that the *chupah* was insufficiently anchored. Sleeping in an outdoor *succah* at night at the onset of a furious storm will give you a keen understanding of what it must be like to cross the Atlantic in a rowboat. There is no doubt about it — wind can be both destructive (winds in Commonwealth Bay, Antarctica, often reach 200 mph) and inconvenient (how do you hold your hat in gale-force winds if you're carrying two suitcases?).

But you cannot live without it. Like so very many things in the world, since we have experienced them from our very first day, we tend to take them totally for granted. Life on earth depends on wind; no one can claim that wind developed from a tadpole that sneezed while crawling from the primeval swamp; therefore it would make sense for us to understand a little about how it operates. The air surrounding the Earth is on the move all the time, and moving air is called wind. What it is that causes air to move is fascinating, all the more so since even now, scientists do not know enough to explain the causes of all winds! The pressure of the air on the Earth's surface varies in different places. This is partly due to the

Wind can be fierce, but without it we couldn't live.

varying amounts of heat they receive. For example: On a warm summer's day, the sun shines on an area, heating up the air. As the temperature increases, the air rises. When air rises it leaves behind an area of lower pressure, because the upward-moving air is not pressing down so firmly on the surface. Areas of high pressure are formed where air is sinking back down, and so pushing down harder. The surface air will then move towards the surrounding lower-pressure area. Thus, if a pressure difference exists, air will move from the higher to the lower-pressure area, in order to even out the pressure.

Around the Earth, there are several major bands where either high or low pressure predominates. There is a general pattern of air movement from the high pressure to the low-pressure areas. The Earth's surface receives the most solar radiation around the equator. The land greatly heats up the air immediately above it, and this vast amount of air rises, leaving a band of predominately low pressure at the surface. This sets up all other air movements. It is interesting that when air moves from high pressure to low pressure, the winds do not take the most direct possible route. They would love to, but are deflected sideways. This is due to the rotating movement of the Earth, and is called the *Coriolis effect*. The forces involved have the effect of deflecting the winds in the northern hemisphere to the right of their intended direction, and those in the southern hemisphere to the left. The Coriolis effect acts on the world's major air movements to determine the directions of the world's major winds.

Without wind, there would be no rain. ("He moves the wind and He makes the rain descend.") Air contains millions of microscopic particles of dust. When moist air rises, expands and cools, any water vapor it contains condenses (turns back into a liquid) onto the surface of the dust particles. This forms minute water droplets, which group together to form clouds. (Never ever complain about dust. Without it there could be no clouds; without clouds, no water; without water, no life. Life — from dust? Yes!) The wind provides the mighty transportation system that moves clouds from places of low requirement (above the sea) to the populated areas where they bring the promise of fertile soil and precious water.

In our age of mechanized transport, it is sometimes easy to forget how in times gone by, wind was the only method of transportation. In 1492, Columbus sailed the ocean blue. After a voyage of some eight weeks, he sighted the American continent. Without wind, his little ship, together with the hope of settling the great continent, would have remained becalmed and landlocked in a Portuguese harbor. Without wind, Australia would have remained the exclusive habitat of aborigines and kangaroos. Without wind, all the goods and materials, all the movements of men and merchandise would have been stalled in the land of their birth.

People are worried about the fact that so-called "fossil fuels" (oil, gas, coal) only exist in limited quantities, and at some undetermined time in the future (precisely when you need your car to go to the *chasunah*), it will all run out. Whether this is a legitimate cause for concern is a matter for speculation, but the fact is that even without any fossil fuels at all, the situation is far from bleak. The potential for using the wind to generate electricity is huge. A recent study for the European Community estimated that there were sufficient suitable sites in Europe to house about 400,000 wind-powered generators — sufficient to provide three times Europe's present energy needs. The people of Fair Isle, off the north coast of Scotland, have already been making use of wind power. They installed a small wind generator in the early 1980s, and have managed to cut electricity bills by more than 75 percent from the old diesel engines. Just in case you are concerned about having a whirling turbine sitting in your back yard, fear not. The British Department of Energy has estimated that clusters of wind turbines built in shallow water around the coast could produce one and a half times Britain's present electricity demand. And, like all the best things in life, wind is free!

Make sure that no one is watching you, and then look down. You will notice a fleshy protuberance jutting out just above your mouth. We call it a nose. A nose has three main functions. One is to inhale and exhale air. The second is to act as a base for your eyeglasses (have you ever wondered how you would wear glasses without a nose?) and the third function is to be able to smell. The ability to detect smell ("*rei-ach*") depends to a large degree on wind ("*ru'ach*"). It is the movement of air that permits molecules to travel distances, and enables us to identify aromas and fragrances. This is not a luxury. The presence of smoke or pungent fumes can be a sign of danger — without wind to bring those molecules to our detection center, we could be at risk. Wind saves lives!

And generates life. If a flowering plant is to reproduce, it must ensure that its pollen reaches the style of another member of the same species. Pollen grains can easily be carried by the wind, and a large number of plants — grasses, conifers, as well as many broad-leaved trees — rely on the wind to do just that. Wind-pollinated trees such as hazel usually produce their tiny flowers (that in turn produce the pollen) early in the year, before they put out their leaves, and as a result, the wind is able to gather the pollen without hindrance, and the grains do not become trapped in the foliage. Who told the hazel to be so farsighted?! Wind is a most effective transporter. It can take the tiny dry grains of pollen as high as 19,000 feet, and carry them 3,000 miles away from their parents. Without wind, many plants would survive for just one generation. With wind, there is life and continuity.

And fresh air! Wind moves air — on the Beaufort scale, Force 1 is the slightest, lightest breeze that can move a column of smoke (which makes the phenomenon of the inability of the Temple Mount's howling wind to move the column of smoke from the *mizbei'ach* all the more miraculous. Wind disperses smog, fumes and stale air. It ensures that we can all enjoy fresh, oxygenated air. Without wind, we would live in a permanently polluted, smoke-filled, fume-drenched ashcan of an atmosphere. Without wind, how could we live? Feel it on your face, fill your lungs with the wonderful wind, watch the clouds scurry across the sky, smell fragrances, watch dandelion seeds afloat on the wind and thank the One Who organizes it all.

T t was a usual Thursday morning, or perhaps it was Monday. The *minyan* convened as usual at 7:15 a.m. and proceeded smoothly. *Shemoneh Esrei* followed *Shema,* which in turn was followed by *Tachanun.* The *chazzan* finished *Tachanun,* and the man who had been appointed to take out the *Sefer Torah* went up the three steps, and opened the curtain of the *Aron Hakodesh.* And then stopped. The reason for the delay was not immediately apparent, and some of the congregants, who could not directly see the *Aron Hakodesh,* reacted with the reflex action common to all Jewish people. They said, *"Nu?"* A few long seconds elapsed, and again nothing transpired, so the *Nu's* spread, growing into a louder, *"Nu? Nu!"* By this time it had become clear what the problem was. The doors of the *Aron Hakodesh* were locked, and the gentleman standing haplessly in front of them did not have the key, nor any idea where the key was. Nor, it seemed, did anyone else. By now, the impatient indignation of the congregation peaked, and a crescendo of *Nu's* spilled over, echoing from wall to wall. Fortunately, there was one clever individual who understood that even a hundred *Nu's* will not open a single door; so he looked into the absent *gabbai's* desk, extracted the elusive bunch of keys, selected the appropriate key and opened the *aron*. The minicrisis was over, the congregants put away their *Nu's* for the next occasion, but when they went home, and their wives asked them, as wives always do, whether there was any *Nu's* in *shul*, they had plenty to tell them!

The moral of the story is that reading from the Torah might well be an integral part of every Thursday morning, and the *Sefer Torah* itself is invaluable, but if it is locked away, and the one little piece of metal that can unlock the door is missing, then the whole process remains stymied. What is true in everyday life is true also in the human body. Your body has two control systems. One is the *nervous system*, which sends messages around the body in the form of nerve signals. The other is the *endocrine system*, which sends messages around the body in the form of chemicals, called *hormones*. Hormones are made in special factories — *glands* — called *hormonal glands*. Each gland releases its hormone directly into the bloodstream. As the blood carries the hormone through the body, the hormone affects the working of specific body parts, called target organs. The higher the level of a hormone in the blood, the greater its effect on its target organs. The hormones are the important keys that unlock the body's vital functions that allow us to live and function normally. Without our hormones, our vital keys to good health, life would be bleak.

It is their size and quantity that blows the mind. Without

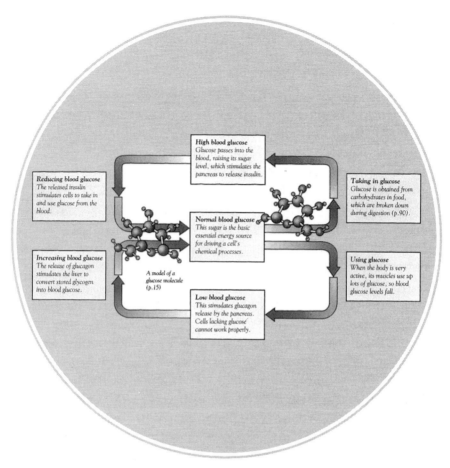

A small example of the vital hormone cycle

a key, you cannot open a locked *Aron Hakodesh*. An *Aron Hakodesh* is quite large and the key is relatively small. But any key, however small, is not insignificant, and if you collect a sufficiently large bunch of them, it would not take too long before they tear a hole in your pocket. The *pituitary gland* is one of the main manufacturers of hormones in the body, and is situated on the underside of the brain. It is probably the most complex organ in the body, and is the size of a single pea, weighing all of one fiftieth of an ounce. It is divided into two lobes, the larger of which produces some 10 hormones. These hormones are among the most complex substances known to man, and the total daily output — of the chemicals that hold the key to normal development and bodily functions — is less than one millionth of a gram. That is the size of your key!

In understanding the wisdom that lies inherent in the construction of the human being, these incredible statistics are all important. You will find the following difficult to believe, but it is true. There is a scientific word describing a process in the human cell that is 207,000 letters long. That makes this single word equal in length to a short novel, or about 80 typed sheets of letter-size paper (approximately 26 times longer than this article). That is a single function of a tinier than tiny cell, one of trillions. If it takes a short novel just to identify a process, how many volumes would it take to explain it? And that is just one single process out of a vast number of processes. When you are dealing with this level of intelligence and wisdom, you begin to perceive something of the Wisdom and Intelligence from Whom it all stems, for intelligence does not come from nothing.

What is even more humbling is that the study of hormones (called endocrinology) did not really begin before the late 19th. century. The very name "hormone" (which comes from the Greek term "to set in motion") was only coined in 1905. For centuries, hormonal glands — which are also called "*ductless glands*" — were virtually ignored by scientists. Doctors thought that the *pituitary gland* was the source of nasal mucus! The secretions were simply too minimal to be detected until the advent of modern chemistry. Thus, vital functions of the body — of which we intelligent humans have been totally ignorant for centuries — have been performing their brilliantly complicated tasks; unsung, quietly and efficiently. It is when we learn how abysmally ignorant we are of the deep wisdom that lies within our very selves that we begin to realize how limited our knowledge really is.

Nobody can will himself to grow or to stop growing. No one can turn off his digestive system simply by thinking about it (try it!) and nobody can cause his cells to reproduce themselves simply by concentrating. Yet all of these changes in the body are just as much under the control of the brain as is the conscious decision whether or not to reach out for an extra helping of *kugel*. It is just that instead of being responses to messages sent along nerve pathways, they are responses to messages delivered by hormones. For example: The pea-sized pituitary produces a hormone called *vasopressin*. It is mainly responsible for maintaining the percentage of water in the blood. The pituitary gland is particularly active in its secretion during hot weather, when there is greater evaporation of water through the skin (perspiration). When the water content of the blood begins to drop below its normal level, the gland is activated to release vasopressin, which stimulates the filter units of the kidneys to absorb more water from the urine. At the same time, sensations of thirst are stimulated, encouraging Mr. Human to increase his fluid intake. Thank you, hormone, for saving us from dehydration.

Everyone knows that in times of stress, the *adrenal glands* — small and helmet shaped, which sit atop the kidneys — release the hormone *adrenaline* which spreads through the blood to its target organ. As a result, your heart beats harder and faster, your lungs breathe more rapidly, blood is diverted from your skin and inner organs to your muscles, your liver releases high-energy glucose to give your body energy, and your digestive system closes down. You can always identify the ones who are going to speak at the *chasunah* — look for the men who are not eating! It is that hormone that gives you the necessary energy and alertness vital for the special performance (no great *darshan* has ever fallen asleep during his own *drashah*, which is more than can be said for the audience). Even in less stressful situations, when the body rests, hormones are at work. The kidneys manufacture a hormone (*erythropoietin*) which stimulates the production of new red blood cells and hemoglobin at the rate of two million each second. Hormones play a vital role in the processes of digestion. Small glands in the lining of the stomach react to the presence of protein-rich foods by secreting the hormone *gastrin,* which stimulates the flow of gastric juices. Other glands in the walls of the intestine release *secretin,* a hormone which helps to control the production of bile by the liver. The same hormone probably stimulates the pancreas to release its digestive juices into the intestine. Your size, tall or short, is affected directly by a hormone called *somatotrophin,* produced and secreted by the front lobe of the amazing pituitary gland. This hormone acts directly to regulate the growth of nearly all bones and tissues, unlike other hormones from the pituitary which regulate the activity of individual glands.

For effective control, two opposing systems are needed. A car needs an accelerator and brakes, and a muscle must have its opposing partner. The hormones too have antagonistic effects. Adrenaline promotes the release of sugar into the blood, while insulin has the opposite effect. The correct balance is maintained by the "feedback" effect of hormones — the system whereby information is relayed to a source, "telling it" about events in the body, and so enabling it to adjust its output accordingly. For example: A pituitary hormone (TSH) stimulates the *thyroid gland* to produce *thyroxine,* which controls the rate of metabolism and growth. But thyroxine production is kept in check by the fact that when thyroxine reaches the pituitary, via the circulation, production of thyroid-stimulating hormone is supressed! A perfect system!

Hormones, the chemical messengers, are breathtaking in their complexity. There are many different hormones, but only a small number have so far been identified. Who can fathom the enormous wisdom inherent in these vital keys to healthy living, and who can fathom the vast Intelligence that constructed it all? At least by gaining an insight into the immeasurable complexity of this one aspect of Creation, it can help us declare with even greater conviction — "*Hodu laHashem ki tov — ki l'olam chasdo.*"

A Matter of Timing

It must have been marvelous to go to school in the olden days. First of all, French grammar had not yet been invented (better still, neither had German grammar), and secondly, you could never be late. Today, every pupil's fear is to arrive at the school gate one minute after 9 o'clock, and hear the sounds of the school bell echoing across the playground. It's useless pleading that the clock is inaccurate, because it is likely to be electrically controlled; accurate to a thousandth of a second. It was not like that in the time of the Egyptians. They either used a shadow clock (the shadow cast by a crossbar on a time scale — marvelous idea, except you had to remember to point the clock east in the morning, and then turn it west in the afternoon) or a water clock. This involved a stone bucket filled with water, with a tiny hole drilled at the bottom of the bucket. The time was indicated by the level of the water against a scale marked on the inside. Apart from this system being the origin of the popular song "There's a hole in my bucket…" it was, as you can imagine, not accurate to the second. King Alfred the Great of England improved matters with his candle clock, but that proved unpopular, largely due to the inconvenience of carrying it around on the wrist.

A 17th century Dutchman by the name of Huygens designed the first practical pendulum clock, and then an even more accurate spring-driven clock, but you have to advance to contemporary times for the last word in accuracy. In 1969, the U.S. Naval Research Laboratory, using the principle of vibrating molecules of ammonia gas, built an ammonia atomic clock. It is accurate to one second in — wait for it — 1,700,000 years!

There is nothing like a watch, with its many coordinated and sensitive parts, to demonstrate the happy marriage of wisdom and design. The very fact that there exists a machine that can mark the passage of time indicates two things. Firstly that time is important, and there are creatures who wish to regulate their lives according to time; and secondly that they have the intelligence to create a mechanism that will measure time accurately. In that respect, the quartz-powered clock on your wrist is no greater an indication of intelligence than the ancient shadow clock of the Egyptians. The principle is the same. What would you say if we could illustrate that there are creatures (man included) that possess a clock — perhaps a biological clock — which accurately measures the passage of time in a manner similar to the most accurate modern timepieces that grace your wrist? Would you agree that it indicates the presence of intelligence and design in the creation of those creatures?

Let us see. February is often the coldest month of the winter. The wind rattles the windows, and the snow deepens on

Have a safe journey, birds. Where's your map?

the land. But, if you listen carefully, you will hear the resonant call of the great horned owl booming across the forest. (City dwellers will have to use their imagination instead of their ears!) Despite the weather, the countdown to spring is under way. That call means that the female owl will soon be sitting low on the nest, warming her white eggs as the snow drifts across her head and back. Timing is crucial, for the owls must time the arrival of their young to the arrival of the bird migration and the appearance of young, awkward mammals, which will provide the little owls with vital food. The tiny owlets will hatch in March, just as the red-winged blackbirds arrive in large numbers. At a time when a young owl must be fed its own weight in food each day (imagine you had to do that!), the owl parents will need only to dip into the fields and marshes to supply the ravenous mouths. Later, when it seems impossible to find enough food to feed the owlets, most of the migrating birds will be coming through the forest and fields, noisy, conspicuous and easy prey. This migration, in turn, has been triggered to reach its destination about the time that insects, other foods and shelter are abundant. And the insects will awaken in time to gnaw on the opening leaves, or, in the case of insect parasites, upon their hosts. Absolute coordination, hair-trigger timing, wondrously planned.

Special timing produces special sights. The amazing behavior of Atlantic eels is unique. Eels spend many years of seemingly contented life in the ponds and streams of Europe and North America. Then suddenly, prompted by a mysterious signal, they leave their homes, go down the rivers and head out into the Atlantic until they reach a great deep in the Atlantic Ocean, south of Bermuda, where they sink and disappear forever. Later, an eruption of tiny, transparent, threadlike creatures with bulging black eyes comes welling up to the surface; spreading out like an ever expanding mushroom, they stream off in two groups — one heading east for Europe, the other going west to America. Each tiny eel knows where it has to go, although it has never been there. Both shoals — by now grown into young eels — swim up the rivers of their respective continents, until they reach the precise place from where their parents started out. What timing mechanism informs the eels on either side of the Atlantic that it is time to travel? Simple it isn't. Clever it most certainly is.

How do you understand the remarkable ability of many birds, who in the pitch darkness of the night, before dawn rises, behave as though they knew how long it would be before sunup? On an overcast morning, as well as when the sky is perfectly clear, a robin hesitantly begins a lonely predawn solo. Who told him that morning was on its way? Who constructed the clock inside him? "Blessed are You, Hashem... Who gave the rooster understanding to distinguish between day and night."

Humans are not so different. Not all regular actions are governed entirely by habit. For some activities, such as eating and sleeping, there seems to be an instinctive timing mechanism built into everyone. (Some people have a remarkable instinct that whenever they sit down to a *shiur*, they fall into a blissful, relaxing slumber!) In a recent experiment to study the internal clock, a volunteer was kept in a permanently lit windowless room with no clock or watch. He soon settled into a routine — asking for food at regular times throughout the day, and sleeping for his normal period of about eight hours every night. Even after several days, his internal biological clock kept him on schedule, his body "knew" what time it was.

Think of a little baby, soon after birth. When doting relatives have their first introduction to the new member of the family, they ("they" being the female gender) make strange faces, even stranger noises ("Gushy bushy mushy"), tickle the defenseless infant's chin, all in a determined effort to induce the child to smile. Imagine what would happen if, when it did smile, it revealed two gleaming rows of teeth! What a surprise everyone would receive! Everyone knows that a child is born fully formed, beautiful — and toothless. Interestingly enough, a baby's teeth begin to form while in the embryo stage, months before birth. At birth, all the deciduous (first set of) teeth are formed, except for their roots. The tips of the first permanent molars are also hardened, although these teeth do not emerge until the child is about 6 years old. Think first of the wisdom. The little baby, drinking his mother's milk, has no need at all for teeth. To the contrary, teeth would be an impediment to mother and baby. So it has none. Then, when it begins to eat, it does not begin with chicken bones and nut kernels. Soft little teeth are adequate, and that's what it receives. Only later, when its diet resembles that of an adult, will it receive its adult set of teeth. Now think of the timing. What mechanism is there in the young baby that announces to the embedded teeth that it is time to emerge? And where is the secret clock that informs the permanent teeth that the time has come to replace the initial set? It must be there somewhere, for it certainly is well timed!

Often, timing is so crucial that it is a lifesaver. Have you ever been driving on a rainy night, overtaking a heavy truck, vision impaired with flying spray, and suddenly needed to sneeze? We wish you better things! It is impossible to sneeze with your eyes open (try it), and during those couple of seconds that your eyes are closed, you are quite literally driving blind. Why, then, do you not experience a similar sensation every time you blink? It is an incredible fact that even if you are engaged in a task that requires maximum concentration, blinking both eyes at one time will never disturb you. Why not? Timing. Your eyelid muscles have been synchronized to blink simultaneously, and at tremendous speed. Your eyelids have an important job to perform — to wash and bathe your eyes with a complex preparation of cleansing fluid and antiseptic. Time allowed for the complete job, including leaving your eyes not too moist (blurred vision) and not too dry (irritating) — a fraction of a second. And it works perfectly, time and time again.

The simplest, most primitive ancient shadow clock offers ample evidence of intelligence. The evidence of the most advanced atomic clock is even more compelling. What would you say to the global clocks and supersophisticated clocks that regulate our own lives and the world around us?

Ma Gadlu Maasecha Hashem!

The Chasan Watch

I t seems that all fathers-in-law are keen that their future sons-in-law should appear under the *chupah* on time. How else do you explain the well-established custom to give the young man a "*chasan zeiger*"? The real question that all aspiring fathers-in-law need to answer is how much to spend on the celebrated timepiece. It is a little like asking how long is a piece of string, for the answer is as variable as the size of your pocket. May we, as an opening offer, suggest a rather fine watch called the "Golconda." In place of the traditional glass face, an old Indian rose-cut Golconda diamond is used through which the handmade Swiss-gold skeleton movement is clearly visible. The bezel (the outer ring around the watch glass) is set with brilliant cut diamonds, and the bracelet is entirely set with 252 diamonds. Each watch is one of a kind. The price? Do you really want to know the price? An insignificant sum, nearly $1 million. Anyone prepared to give that caliber of watch to his son-in-law must hold him in high regard, or perhaps not hold him in such high regard, but just have lots of money.

The truth is that whatever the price of a watch, it is value for money. Some watches are items of jewelry in their own right, but even the plainest of timepieces is a high precision instrument. In the tiniest of spaces (you can buy a watch just over half an inch long, a quarter of an inch wide, and not much thicker than a piece of paper) will be packed a maze of complex working parts. You can have a watch that is shock proof, water resistant, tells you the time in two time zones, lights up in the dark, informs you of the date, year, phase of the moon — it will do everything apart from making you a cup of tea in the morning. In some good watches, especially chronographs (a watch with an independent stop-start mechanism used for short interval timing) and complicated models, as many as six different types of special oil and grease need to be used on a single movement. And then there is the Emergency watch. This is designed to save the lives of pilots and other aviators who may need to summon emergency services. In a real emergency, a large button on the case is unscrewed so that an aerial can be pulled out of the case which in turn activates a miniature radio transmitter inside the watch. Just the thing for *chasanim* running late. Amazing! Where else will you find such superlative design in so confined a space? Only in the human body.

If you are able to read this article, you are making use of one of the most sophisticated and wonderful cameras imaginable. Your two eyes provide an incredibly detailed, constantly updated, three-dimensional color view of the world. In an area no larger than a Ping-Pong ball, there are

A selection of the world's finest watches

tens of millions of electrical connections capable of handling 1.5 million simultaneous messages. The poor watch — with all its diamonds — is already beginning to feel inferior, but let us examine the eye in some greater detail.

The very front of your eye — the domed front window — is called the *cornea.* It is a transparent disc, curved to the shape of the eye, allowing the light rays which pass through to refract (bend), causing the rays to converge. Even though the cornea is transparent, it still contains nerve endings. Wonder of wonders! How do you construct transparent nerves! it's rather like producing invisible electric cables that lead to the middle of a pane of glass to allow you to insert an electric plug in your window — how could you do it? When stimulated, the function of the nerve endings in the cornea is to cause reflex blinking, the secretion of tears, and to produce the sensation of pain. When you peel onions, and experience the tears, blinking and stinging eyes (all of which serve to protect your eyes from the noxious fumes of the onion), you can thank the invisible nerves in your cornea for the early-warning system.

Just a mere quarter of an inch or so behind the cornea lies the *lens.* "Suspended" might be a better way of describing the remarkable positioning of this transparent, ribbonlike bundle of fibers that continue the focusing of the light rays which the cornea began. The fibrous material in the center of the lens has a greater refractive power than that at the edges, and this property enables it to produce a sharper image than could a simple glass lens. Who needs to get excited about an old Indian rose-cut Golconda diamond in place of the traditional glass in the million dollar watch, when in your twin wonder-cameras you have a living lens, superior to any glass, capable of altering its shape to accommodate rays of light from differing distances, composed of cells that are constantly replacing themselves.

Even though the shape of the eye resembles a Ping-Pong ball, that is where the resemblance ends. The little plastic ball is full of air, whereas the eye is full of fluid. Since the lens with its attendant muscles stretches across the eye, the eye is effectively composed of two chambers — in front of the lens, extending to the cornea, and behind the lens, reaching to the screen (the *retina*) at the rear of the orb. The liquid which fills the eye in front of the lens has the name *aqueous humor.* It is a watery solution, containing dissolved salts and glucose, having a composition similar to blood plasma, although there is more sodium and chloride and less urea than in plasma. This remarkable solution performs three vital functions. It holds the front of the eye in its rigid shape (if it did not, there would be dramatic distortion of the light rays

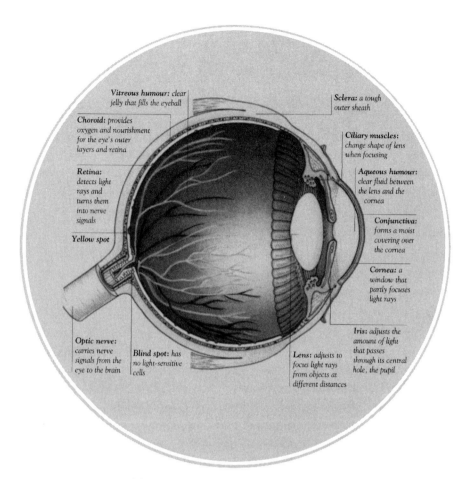

A cross-section of the eye. How much would you pay for this beautiful machine?

entering the eye), it helps to refract the light that enters the eye, and it nourishes its neighbors. it contains dissolved oxygen, and supplies the lens and cornea, which do not have blood vessels, with nutrients and oxygen. Now isn't that thoughtful? Talk about coordinated planning. The lens and the cornea must be transparent, to allow for free passage of light. Blood vessels would obscure the transparent quality of the cornea and the lens, but they are living organs, and they need food! Blood vessels are the highways of the transport system that supplies vital nutrition to every cell. No vessels, no food. Enter the aqueous humor to save the day. Here you have a novel variation of the old question. Which came first — the aqueous humor or the lens? Lens without humor cannot survive. Humor without lens makes no sense. The answer? Both were created simultaneously as part of a coordinated complete system.

If you are blessed with an inquiring mind, you will ask the following question. Granted, the aqueous humor provides all the nutritional needs of the cornea and the lens, but where is it produced? The answer is fascinating. The lens is suspended by suspensory ligaments. These in turn are anchored to an area of thickened fiber called the *ciliary body,* which contains both the muscles that control the curvature of the lens during accommodation, and also houses the factories that produce the wonder food that feeds the lens and the cornea. it is hard to believe, but when you look into someone's eyes, not only are you staring into two of the most sophisticated cameras imaginable, but you are looking at complex food factories situated within the eye itself. Not even the most expensive watch produces its own oil!

Wherever liquid is produced, there has to be a drainage channel nearby to allow for the excess fluid to be removed. What applies to the gutter on your roof applies both to the throat at the back of your mouth and to your two eyes. The aqueous humor that is so skillfully produced by the ciliary body drains into a circular canal (called the *Canal of Schlemm*) which runs around the cornea, and which itself empties into the *venous* (vein) *system.* What would happen if there was no adequate drainage system? If, for any reason, the Canal of Schlemm (presumably named after the gentleman who discovered it) is narrowed or blocked, or else more fluid is produced than can flow away, the result is a serious condition known as *glaucoma.* The fluid accumulates in the eye, exerting pressure on the optic nerve, which in turn can reduce the blood supply. The symptoms are colored halos around bright lights, loss of side vision, difficulty of adjusting to the dark, or a blurring of vision. Doctors can check for glaucoma simply by pressing a little gadget called a tonometer against the eyeball. Again, the question is relevant. Which came first, the drainage channel or the liquid?

Charles Darwin wrote that if it could be demonstrated that any complex organ existed which could not possibly have been formed by numerous successive slight modifications, his theory (of *apikorsus*) would absolutely break down. The eye must have made him shudder. It is quite evident that if any of the numerous components of the eye were to go wrong, or were missing, an image would not be produced, and the eye would not work. It either functions as a whole, or not at all. Half an eye is no eye. There is no survival value in an eye that doesn't see! The Canal of Schlemm is more than a discovery — it is an eloquent example of a coordinated structure of enormous complexity whose wisdom is far beyond our ability to comprehend. It all points to a unified design.

Chasanim — wear your watch with happiness, and enjoy its complexity. And compare. A watch contains 41 moving parts. An eye has at least 137 MILLION separate components in the retina that record light and transmit electrical impulses through the optic nerve to the brain — and that is just one section of the eye. Watch your watch with your eyes, and think of the genius of co-ordination that lies in them, as in all of Creation.

Se'u marom eineichem u'reu Mi bara eileh.

The Super-Chemist

"**D**ouble double toil and trouble; Fire burn and cauldron bubble." Those familiar with English literature will recognize these immortal lines as the incantation recited by a bunch of evil witches as they prepared their foul brew. You can just picture them — three cackling old crones, nose and chin almost meeting, throwing frogs' legs into a steaming cauldron while clutching an oversized "Witch Magazine" in which the dreadful formula lay written. If this is the popular view of the chemist shop of old, things have certainly improved. Firstly, witches are no longer employed, and secondly, frogs' legs are protected by a preservation order!

Seriously however, everyone knows that in order to dispense drugs and medicines, whether homeopathic or conventional, either in a hospital or in a store, great expertise is required. In order to qualify as a pharmacist, a student has to complete years of study on anatomy identical to that of a medical student. What might be good for the heart could be harmful for the lungs. The cause of a stomach ache needs to be determined before it can be treated. In addition, the hopeful pharmacist needs to have a thorough knowledge of chemistry, and how different compounds and substances react and blend with each other. Old remedies, as well as modern drugs, are made with chemicals obtained from rocks, plants, the sea, coal and oil. Without expert knowledge of the nature of these materials, he is more likely to create an explosion than a cure. The gentleman you see working behind the counter in his white coat is no witch doctor. In fact he knows nothing about spells and incantations. Through hard work and dedication, he has gained a thorough knowledge of many aspects of science, and his expertise allows him to be of great benefit to mankind. What would you say if you were shown plants and animals, whose intelligence is somewhat akin to those frogs' legs, yet are able to produce chemical compounds and substances so complex that no pharmacist could compete?

The most widespread method of protection that has been given to leaves is neither physical nor mechanical, but chemical. Plants manufacture substances that, in one way or another, deter their attackers. Some of the techniques are astonishingly sophisticated. There is a wild species of South American potato that discharges a message-chemical. This is called a *pheromone,* and it is the same chemical emitted by *aphids* when they are under attack. This deters the aphids (little creatures that love to nibble and destroy the leaves of the South American potato plant) and they never land on it. There is the *African bugleweed plant* that does something even more amazing. Within its tissues, it synthesizes a substance similar to the hormone that controls the development of caterpillars. If a caterpillar is foolish enough to eat this substance, then when it turns into a butterfly, it will develop two heads, and perish. Not surprisingly, caterpillars avoid the bugleweed!

When some leaves are nibbled by a foraging insect, they produce chemicals that either give the bug indigestion or make it feel falsely sated. When some species of caterpillars munch the leaves, the plants emit chemicals that attract parasitic wasps. The wasps lay eggs in the caterpillars, and the developing larvae eat their hosts. The plant is happy.

Many plants use a straightforward chemical defense — poison. *Bracken,* the most widespread of ferns in Britain, fills its young tender leaves with cyanide. Very few insects are able to tolerate it, and most are deterred. By the time the leaves are mature and so tough that they seem likely to be of interest to larger grazing animals, such as rabbits and deer, the plant has manufactured a cocktail of poisons so powerful that they can cause blindness and fatal illnesses in mammals. Due to this, and an ability to spread by proliferating underground stems, bracken is able to dominate huge areas of hillside. Expert pharmacist? You've heard nothing yet!

Listen to this. The African *acacia trees,* well protected though they may be by their thorns, use distasteful chemicals in their leaves as a second line of defense. Furthermore, and more remarkably, they warn each other that they are doing so. At the same time as they fill their leaves with poison, they release ethylene gas which drifts out of the pores of their leaves. Other acacias within 50 yards are able to detect this gas, and as soon as they do so, they themselves immediately begin to manufacture poison and distribute it to their leaves. A browsing animal soon finds that the tree it first attacked is no longer fit to eat and moves away. But it has now to go some distance, for the rest of the acacias nearby have been forewarned — and are now forearmed.

Ever been for a walk in the countryside and been stung by

a *nettle?* If we understand the wisdom demonstrated by this plant, it might help us to sympathize more readily with the victim. The nettle's sting is a minute glassy hypodermic needle, which, if given even the slightest touch, breaks off. The broken edges are so sharp that they can cut skin. If that were not bad enough, at the same time a poison held in a small chamber at the bottom of the needle squirts into the wound. The poison is extremely effective — and painful. And not only to humans. Rabbits too have very sensitive noses, and they have learned to leave nettles strictly alone. Australia has been blessed with even more ferocious stingers. One is a tree that can grow to 50 feet tall. A traveler failing to recognize the large and characteristic heart-shaped leaves, and brushing past them, is likely to be so badly stung that he may have to be taken to a hospital. The poison, like that of the nettle, contains histamine, but also other unidentified venoms that can cause intense pain that lasts for weeks. The pharmacists know their job!

When it comes to defense mechanisms that include poisons, the mind turns (reluctantly) to spiders and snakes. There are in fact many animals that produce venom. Venom is any toxic secretion produced by animals, used either for attack or defense. You will be pleased to know that venomous species are found in many animal groups, but few are dangerous to humans. Exceptions include certain snakes, scorpions, spiders and jellyfishes. The effects of venoms on the prey include violent inflammations, widespread hemorrhage, and unpleasant effects on the nervous system. Interested in more detail?

There was a famous Spanish explorer by the name of Fernandez de Oviedo. In the year 1535 he went exploring in South America, and reported: "There are spiders of marvelous bigness ... bigger than a man's hand." He may have been describing the South American goliath bird-eater, which really is as big as a man's hand. Known more popularly (or unpopularly) as the *tarantula,* they are by and large timid creatures. They are certainly venomous (details to follow) but they rarely bite people. Medical literature does not contain a single reliable report of a fatality from the venom. But they really are amazing creatures. They have airborne defenses. With a flick of a hind leg, tarantulas defend themselves by launching tiny hairs bristling with microscopic barbs. Once embedded in the attacker's skin or eyes, the barbs cause a maddening itch that can persist for months. Hollow fangs deliver venom produced in adjacent tiny bulbs. This produces burning and swelling that lasts a few hours, and could be fatal for a small animal. Help!

Next time you visit a zoo, visit the Reptile House, and try and find a *Poison Arrow Frog.* These tiny frogs live in the rain forests of South America, and their bright and beautiful colors say one thing: "Don't eat me, I'm poisonous!" They are little, about the size of your middle finger, but from their skin comes the most potent poison that can be made by any animal. One tiny frog, the size of your thumb, carries enough poison to annihilate 20,000 mice! South American Indians dip their arrows in frog poison. Once a monkey or a jaguar has been scratched with a poisoned arrow, the hunters follow it through the jungle, waiting for it to succumb. Sweet customs! These little frogs taste foul. Any bird unlucky enough to try and eat one will spit it out in hurry, and learn to stay clear of tiny colorful — and deadly — frogs in the future.

After having been introduced to some of the pharmacists of the plant and animal world, certain observations become apparent. All the devices employed by trees and animals are exceedingly complex. In order for the nettle to produce its irritating poison, it has available precisely the same ingredients as the apple tree has to produce apples. And they are very simple — earth, sunshine and rain. In addition, the nettle needs to have knowledge of hypodermic needles, the nervous system, and human likes and dislikes. What would happen if people just loved to be stung by nettles? When reptiles and insects produce poison, they themselves must have a built-in immunity in order to survive. Which came first, the immunity to a poison that had not yet been developed, or the poison without the immunity? In addition, the poison must be full strength. Diluted venom would be a useless encumbrance, as would venom without the fangs. Who told the animals just how strong to make their venom? You, dear reader, are intelligent. Could you unilaterally grow a machine gun out of your forehead, complete with replaceable bullets? The snake is less intelligent than you. How did it manage? What is the source of this vast intelligence?

The more you hear, the more you think, and the clearer it becomes. No pharmacist becomes a pharmacist by accident. One must study and gain knowledge and qualifications. These lesser known botanical and zoological pharmacists, with their sophisticated expertise, have been trained by the greatest expert of all — the Creator of Everything.

"Baruch oseh ma'aseh Bereishis ..."

The Happiness Machine

I t is an interesting phenomenon of the Jewish world that as soon as you hear that someone is traveling, you feel compelled to think of something to send with him. It doesn't really matter where the person is going, it could be from Vancouver to Vladivostok, you'll quickly discover a distant relative in that far-off city who is desperate for a packet of cheese and a pair of socks. This phenomenon is particularly prevalent amongst those traveling to *Eretz Yisrael*. It could be something to do with the fact that when *Bnei Yisrael* left Egypt, no one traveled with less than 90 donkeys piled high with booty — for ever since, whenever we hear of someone fortunate enough to be on their way to the Holy Land, we feel compelled to give him a few packages "*zecher l'yetzias Mitzrayim.*" The concept of traveling light — the suave business man striding off the plane with his one slim attache case — can never apply to a *Yid.* No sooner have you so much as thought of traveling, the telephone will be jangling with your many friends asking whether you have room for "something small," and asking when they can bring it! For some strange reason, it seems that we *Yidden* have not heard of the postal system.

This is a shame, for most of the world's population could communicate with almost anyone anywhere by mail within a few days. Asking someone to take an envelope with them is fraught with risks. It can (and often does) remain in the traveler's pocket for weeks, neglected and forlorn, whereas popping it into a mailbox virtually guarantees its safe arrival within days. Whether you have your letter or package delivered personally, or by mail, there is nothing as wonderful, or as efficient, as communication by your very own voice.

Think of it as if you had never thought of it before. You wish to invite someone to a *sheva berachos.* You go to the person's house, knock on his door. He now stands before you. You open your mouth, and breathe out. Mentally, you activate some special mechanism in your throat that makes the air vibrate in a specific manner. Invisibly, and at a speed of 760 miles per hour, the vibrating air shoots across space towards your friend. It collides with his nose, but nothing registers. It bounces off his forehead, with no ill effect. Fortunately, your friend has been invested with a pair of ears. The vibrating air enters his ears, and, after an incredible journey through skin, bone and fluid, is electrically trans-mitted to his brain which in turn interprets the message. Using specialized muscles, he turns the corners of his mouth upward in an internationally recognized gesture of pleasure (called a "smile"), and in response emits a movement of air at 760 miles per hour towards you, which your master computer interprets as meaning "Thanks so much!"

Speech is remarkable. You just have to think about it. Consider the *Shabbos Hagadol drashah*. One man stands in front of a large crowd. By skillful use of his throat machinery, he transmits invisible but highly meaningful messages to his eager audience. Why is it that sound travels so fast? It was not until 1947 that an American plane was able to break the sound barrier — and here are microscopic molecules of air knocking into each other so fast that the wave pattern of air that carries the sound travels from one end of the room to the other in a split second! Imagine that sound would travel only as fast as you can walk. How would communication be possible? The designer of the ear (and the voice) must have known how fast sound travels through air, otherwise the whole machine would have been pretty useless. The congregants sit, attentive, absorbing the sound waves that convey such vital information. Watch the speaker's mouth — can you see the words being emitted? Speech is as invisible as air, as strong as a hammer, as precious as gold, and a wonder which we should never tire of appreciating. But of what use would precious speech be without the receiving mechanism that we call ears?

Have you ever wondered why you have two ears? Why do we not have a single rotating ear situated atop our heads, rather like the rotating radar dish that characterizes airport control towers? The answer is interesting. When sound waves arrive at one side of your head, they reach one of your ears slightly before the other. The actual time gap is less than one thousandth of a second. Not a long time, but sufficient to allow your ears and brain to detect this time difference and discern the sound's direction. Inside the intricate working of the ear, there are many fine details which make all the difference between being able to hear and not. Sound waves pass along the ear canal to the eardrum, a piece of thin skin (who told it to be thin?) about the size of your little fingernail. Vibrating air (sound waves) hit the eardrum and cause it to vibrate. As you know from a violin string, or the surface

"Are you listening? I'm talking!" Nothing is more effective than communication.

of a drum, if the string or parchment is slack, no vibration will result. A surface, or string, must be taut if it is to be effective. Fortunately (!) a muscle, called the *tensor tympani,* running from the eardrum to the wall of the middle ear maintains a tension in the eardrum by pulling it inwards. The eardrum is so sensitive to vibrations that a whisper from across the room will set your eardrum vibrating — all of a billionth of a centimeter. This minute displacement is sufficient for the wonderful sequence of events to proceed.

The vibrations pass through the eardrum to the middle ear, in which three minuscule bones (*ossicles*), acting as levers, amplify the vibration 22 times and in turn transmit vibrations to the inner ear via an oval window which is attached to the last of the little bones. It is important to understand just how fine and delicate is the design of these, the smallest three bones in your body, and the only bones that do not grow from the day you were born. Each bone is independent of the other two, and moves freely. Each miniature bone is held in place by ligaments and muscles. It is only due to the fact that each one is strategically positioned relative to the other two that they can all act in concert, faithfully transmitting the vital vibrations from the eardrum to the inner ear.

There is one other little question. Once the tiny bones are set into motion, why do they not continue vibrating for a considerable amount of time, rather like tuning forks? If indeed they would do that, and there is no logical reason why they should not, every sound received would continue unabated, becoming ever fainter, but blurring all the sounds together and making clear communication virtually impossible! Pianists will know that one of the pedals at the foot of their instrument is called a "damper," which, when depressed, presses a piece of wood covered with felt against the vibrating string, arresting its movement, giving a clear, crisp sound. You will be pleased to know that your ossicles stop vibrating almost instantly. The reason? The muscle attached to the last of the bones (*stapes*) pulls the stapes away from the oval window, and effectively damps the vibrations immediately after the transmission, giving you clear, cogent sound. This very small muscle has also been designed to incorporate a reflex action, which, should you hear a sudden loud noise, will dampen the violent vibrations of the stapes to save you from the shock that an undamped transmission would give you.

If you like to be where the action is, then the inner ear is the place to be. Safe and secure, surrounded by the toughest bone in the body, dwells the audio-electrical wonder known as the *cochlea*. The snail-shaped cochlea, filled with fluid, is studded with thousands of microscopic hair-shaped nerve cells, each one tuned to a particular vibration. When the stapes knock on the oval window, vibrations ripple through the fluid inside the cochlea. This in turn pulls the tiny hairs, generating a wisp of an electric current, which passes through the auditory nerve to the brain. Just one of its wonders is the following. Vibration of the oval window generates pressure waves in the fluid filling the cochlea. Since you cannot compress liquids, how will this increase in pressure be accommodated? Will it not cause pain or damage? Fortunately not, for at the far end of the coiled cochlea there is another aperture, called "the round window." The change in pressure in the cochlea can now be relieved by the membrane of the round window bulging in or out. Both tiny windows, the oval and the round, enable us to hear. One without the other could not function and would make no sense. They must have come in conjunction with each other.

It is surely no accident that the mouth and ears are close together. Imagine that your ears hung from your ankles, and someone wanted to whisper a secret "for your ears only." It would be mighty uncomfortable crawling on the floor every time you wished to convey some classified information! One of the fascinating features of the voice is the difference in tone between ladies and men's voices. For some reason, a deep tone has a more authoritative ring than a high-pitched sound. If we allow that men's role in the world is to be one of leadership and command, then it makes perfect sense that their voices reflect that role. Male children, on the other hand, who do not yet have that responsibility, have no need for the trappings of authority. Conversely, gentleness and tenderness are feminine attributes, and their voices reflect their equally important, but totally different role in society. Imagine a mother trying to soothe her crying infant in a rough, gruff, deep baritone! The poor child would be scared out of its crib!

Since the magnificent machinery of speech and hearing were supplied free of charge, how about utilizing it? Next time you meet a fellow Jew in the street, use your facial muscles to smile, and your voice to say "Good morning!" — and observe the reaction. An invisible letter of encouragement races through the air at 760 mph, enters his ears, and in a flash, and for free, you have transformed his day, given happiness to a fellow Yid, and *nachas* to the Creator of it all.

The Bright Spark

A talented writer once gave an interesting and novel example to demonstrate the importance of each and every individual, however humble they may think them-selves. Onc upon a tim thr was a man who ndd a typwritr, but was low on financs. Accordingly, h wnt to a scond-hand shop whr a narly nw typwritr was dis-playd. The propritor told him that it was in prfct condition, apart from just on lttr that was missing from th kyboard. Th customr thought, "*Nu*, what can happn if one littl lttr is missing, popl will hardly notic!" and, fling vry plasd with himslf, h bought th machin. Poor man — it didn't tak him vry long to discovr that vry singl lttr, just lik vry singl prson, is ncssary, and its absnc is missd. Fortunately, he soon had it repaired, and sanity, not to mention decipherability, was soon restored.

If the absence of a single letter is so noticeable, what would you say to the absence of all implements powered by something beginning with "e"? Imagine. You wake up in the morning, late, because your battery-powered alarm clock failed to work. From the radio that you keep in your bedroom — silence. Remarkable thing silence; you can actually think! No doom and gloom to distract your thoughts during *davening!* You notice that the house is cold. Of course, there is no electronic pump or thermostat to activate the central heating. You shiver to the bathroom in the dark — no lights — only to realize that your new ultrasophisticated electric toothbrush is as much use without electricity as a car without gasoline. Feeling by now thoroughly miserable, you stumble downstairs. A growing puddle of water under the freezer and next to the fridge tells you what is happening, and your nose confirms that the fresh frozen food that filled it to overflowing was now neither frozen nor too fresh. You felt like weeping, but realizing that it would only add to the indoor lake, you restrained yourself. With one glance you surveyed the sorry scene. A huge pile of laundry — without a washing machine; a mountain of dishes — with no electric dishwasher; carpets full of crumbs — and no vacuum cleaner; pantry full of flour — and no mixer to make dough. No cooker to warm the food, no kettle to heat water, and the greatest tragedy of all, no toast for breakfast. No car to take you to work (in fact, no public transport of any type except hang-gliders, sailing boats, and feet), and no phone to cry into. Even if the electrician came, you wouldn't hear him, for your electric bell is out of order. Even if he knocked on the door, he couldn't help you, for his power drill, his electric screwdriver and his battery-operated flashlight would be useless without electricity. What a life!

Can you imagine life without electricity? It is always difficult to fully appreciate something that you have always

The inside of an atom

had, and never had to manage without. At the same time, however, something as basic and commonplace as electricity deserves a second look. But wait a minute — why should we need to understand electricity? The vast majority of mankind is perfectly content to have the benefit of something without feeling the need to plumb the depths of understanding how it works. You don't have to be conversant with the internal combustion engine to know how to drive, nor a master carpenter to sit on a chair. Electricity, however, is different, for it is part of the created world, and as such a greater insight into the basic nature of electricity can lead to a greater appreciation of the Creator. The surprising thing is that it is nowhere near as complicated as people imagine.

Imagine that you had a piece of meat sitting on the table in front of you. Pick up your knife and fork, and cut the meat in two. Then again, and again. What is the smallest piece that can be obtained? Most people would say an atom. Atoms are the tiny units that make up everything physical. Each atom consists of a central nucleus, or core, with even tinier particles clustered in and around it. These tinier than tiny particles are called neutrons, protons and electrons. At the heart of the atom is a nucleus, which contains the protons and neutrons. Electrons spin around the nucleus in different energy levels. What is the difference between these three types of particles? The answer is that each one has a different sort of electric charge. In exactly the same way that a magnet exerts a magnetic influence on objects around it (attracting some, and repelling others), so every particle exerts an electrical influence. This electrical influence is not necessarily the same (in just the same way as one end of a magnet is North seeking, and the other end is South seeking). A particle with a positive electrical charge is called a *proton;* one with a negative charge is called an *electron;* and a particle with a neutral charge is the *neutron.* The nucleus makes up most of the weight of an atom; but it is the number of electrons and the pattern they form around the nucleus which decide how that atom behaves.

Normally, the total negative electric charge on the electrons circling around a nucleus is exactly balanced by an equal and opposite positive charge in the nucleus, so the electrical charge of that atom is not noticeable. Why is this important? Because the science of electricity and electronics depends on finding ways of upsetting this balance! For example, copper has 29 electrons arranged in four orbiting paths, and the outer shell contains only one electron. As this one is relatively far from the nucleus, there is only a weak attractive force between its negative charge and the positive charge of the nucleus. This outermost electron can easily be persuaded to leave its orbit and travel towards any other positive charge nearby. If this happens, the atom is one electron short, which means that it also lacks one unit of negative charge. The electrical balance is upset, and the atom is now said to have an overall positive charge.

Whenever an electric current (from the mains or from a battery) passes along a copper wire, what you actually have is the movement of millions of electrons. When you remember that there are millions of atoms in the period at the end of this sentence, and that electrons are much tinier than atoms, it seem unbelievable that they can exercise any influence at all. But it is the combined effect of their countless tiny electric charges which makes possible the operation of giant power stations, and indeed all forms of electric current. Bear in mind also that the movement of electrons from one atom to another happens rather quickly. Electric signals travel along wires at speeds almost as fast as light, which is the fastest thing in the universe. Electricity travels at about 179,640 miles per second! Think about it!

Nothing in the created world is accidental. If every atom had an identical structure, for example, if every substance resembled copper, then everything would be transferring electricity to everything else, which in the case of static electricity (non-moving electric charge) would not be too bad. However, in the case of electric current, it would be fatal. Keep calm, because some substances are very poor conductors of electricity. There is a metal, for example, called *germanium,* which has exactly the same electron structure as copper, except in the outer orbit, where it has four electrons instead of one. This difference makes it a poor conductor, because the combined negative charges of the four outer electrons bind them far more closely to the nucleus than was the case with the single outer electron of the copper atom. These electrons are therefore hard to shift out of orbit, and very little current passes through. All substances with tightly bound outer electrons are poor conductors. Some, such as glass, plastic and porcelain, have outer electrons that are even harder to shift than germanium, and these substances are called insulators. Now you know why electric cable can be swathed in plastic insulation, and handled safely. Not an accident.

It is indeed a humbling thought that one speck of dust contains millions of atoms; that each atom contains protons and electrons, and it is the electrical influence of these less than minute particles of matter that powers so much of our modern world. Electricity is quite some discovery! So think. It's possible that this is the very first time that you have tried (and perhaps even succeeded) to understand what electricity is. How then do you account for the fact that your very own body makes use of electricity in countless ways? The sense of hearing operates by converting vibrations into electrical impulses. The sense of smell works by transforming chemical reactions (molecules of matter reacting on a special pad at the top end of your nose) into electrical messages relayed and interpreted in your brain. Touch, sight, and taste all operate by electricity. When is the last time that you changed your battery? Have you ever blown a fuse? If you haven't yet worked out how to change a plug, how do you account for the vastly sophisticated circuitry inside your brain? If the secret of electrons was only discovered in 1897 (by an Englishman [of course!], Sir Joseph Thomson), who taught the human body (and animals for that matter) the secrets of electrons that they have been utilizing so successfully since Creation?

You don't have to be too bright a spark to realize that the One Who created atoms with their unique electrical power is the One Who designed and created the human machine that so efficiently makes use of this amazing power. The evidence of the Creator is everywhere. You only have to know where to look. Open your eyes, use some electricity, and see for yourself.

More Precious Than Gold

When people wake up in the morning, the first thing that they do is grope for the alarm clock to silence its strident ringing. As the inescapable obligation of getting out of bed grows to crisis level, and the valiant decision to get up is made, the same fingers feel for the eyeglasses lying on the night table. The brain behind the fingers expects the glasses to be there. In the same way that you know with confidence that your nose and ears have not moved overnight (indeed very few people check in the mirror), you presume that all your possessions — eyeglasses, shoes, tefillin, car — are in precisely the spot that you previously left them. That is the law of expectation, that all your previous experience in the past has confirmed, that this is how it has to be. The same law applies to many of the things that we blithely take for granted: that your fingernails will grow at a faster rate than your toenails, that your friends will greet you in the street, that the sun will shine in summer — and that there will always be water flowing from the faucet. Now you can manage without an alarm clock; you can grope without your glasses; you could even conceivably cope without a car — but life without water is impossible to imagine. It would be well worth the effort to investigate, and appreciate the most precious of all liquids.

Would you believe just how much water you actually use? The average home in the United States uses 107,000 gallons (486,000 liters) of water every year. In the course of the average day, our modern man will brush his teeth (2 gallons), take a bath (20 gallons), operate his dishwasher (8 gallons), apart from cooking, drinking, washing his clothes and several visits to the bathroom. Not everyone is as affluent. In rural Ghana, for example, a family of four uses on average only 4 gallons a day, or less than the water it takes to flush a toilet. But these figures pale beside the amounts of water that industry uses. Just think: 40,000 gallons of water are used to clean and mill a ton of raw wool, and transform it into cloth. Compute these figures into a national need, and the figures flood the imagination. Niagara Falls carries 19 billion gallons of water over its brink every day. It would take the thundering flow of Niagara 17 days to fill up the 21 main reservoirs that New York City relies upon. Every single day, New York city consumes almost 1 1/2 billion gallons. That's a lot of water.

It does not end there. You need to eat. Farming too is thirsty work, demanding enormous amounts of water, in the form of rainfall or irrigation, not only for the actual growth of the plants, but also for applying fertilizers and pesticides. For example, growing 2 pounds of cherries takes the staggering amount of 715 gallons of water! Water is something that you cannot do without. There is no living thing that does not contain some water. Plants need water to carry out photosynthesis (converting sunshine into energy), and animals need water for digesting food, eliminating waste, and for circulating blood. A lettuce leaf is 94 percent water, a pine tree 55 percent, while you yourself are a dripping 60-70 percent water.

Since everything on earth requires so much water, it comes as no surprise that there is indeed so much of it. Water is the most common chemical compound on Earth. There is so much of it that if the Earth's surface were made absolutely level, the oceans would cover the entire planet to a uniform depth of almost 1.5 miles. What amazes most people is that the oceans hold 97 percent of the world's water. Two percent is frozen in the polar icecaps. The remaining 1 percent not only provides all the water we use, but also includes all the lakes and rivers of the world, all the water in the atmosphere and all the water in the ground! We actually depend on the constant recycling of that 1 percent of water to meet all our needs. All the water in the world's atmosphere only equals about 10 days' normal rainfall. You can imagine that if water was something we used up like gas or oil, then the world would run dry very quickly indeed. Worry not! Thanks to the water cycle (and the One Who organizes it), water does not get used up — it simply goes round and round.

Apart from its abundance, water has many remarkable properties. More substances will dissolve into water than into any other liquid. Since water constitutes about 92 percent of one's blood, and provides the means of transporting nutrients, sugars, acids, salts, minerals and proteins around the body, this ability is vital to life. What gives water this crucial capability? Water molecules have an unusual arrangement of atoms that turns them into miniature "magnets," with a positive electrical charge at one end, and a negative one on the other. Since opposite electrical charges attract, this means that one or the other side of the water molecule will attach itself to molecules of other substances, whatever their charge. For example, compounds as different as salt, sugar and alcohol all dissolve easily in water. Water is extremely "sticky" in this sense, and it dissolves other materials by tearing their molecules away from one another. The fact that water is indispensable to cooking (try making *cholent,* chicken soup or gefilte fish without water!) is known to every housewife. The atomic properties are not known to as many people, yet our very lives depend on water's fantastic qualities.

And don't forget the fish. The fish would like to give a vote of thanks to water (and its Creator) for allowing them to swim safely throughout the winter without freezing solid in the ice. Water is unusual in the way it freezes. Most liquids freeze from the bottom up; as they are cooled, their density increases steadily. This means that warmer layers, being lighter, will always rise, and the coolest liquid will gather at the base. So it is with water — the hottest water in your hot-water tank will be at the top, not the reverse. Yet, ice forms first on the surface of a body of water. For example, the temperature of a lake may be 50 degrees Fahrenheit in autumn. As the cold air of winter begins to cool the lake, the top layer of water will become denser and sink to the bottom. Unlike other liquids, though, water reaches its maximum density at 39 degrees Fahrenheit (4 degrees Celsius) — well above the freezing point. So, at this temperature, the movement of water in the lake will stop. The top layer will cool further, becoming less dense, but will not sink, because the water below it is denser. If the air is cold enough, the water at the surface will then approach the freezing point and become ice. This layer of ice will shield the lake from the cold atmosphere, and thus prevent it from freezing solid.

What makes water behave in this unusual manner? Most solid substances are denser than their liquid form. To form a solid, molecules come close to each other and link up. But when water molecules (one oxygen atom with two hydrogen atoms attached) link to form the regular patter of an ice crystal, their odd shape creates a gap between them, increasing the amount of space they take up. Ice is therefore less dense than water — which is why ice cubes float! Fish of the world, rejoice!

On a hot day, a tall tree can lose several hundred gallons of water in the form of vapor from its leaves. If those leaves are to be prevented from wilting, that water has to be continuously replaced. The tree has to gather it with its roots, lift it several scores of feet in its trunk, and send it along its branches and twigs into the leaves themselves. A fireman, perched on top of his tallest ladder, can only get water into his hose if it is pumped up by a huge vibrating engine roaring away on the ground beneath. Yet a tree manages to do a similar thing with no visible movement and in total silence. How? We return to the unusual electrical qualities of water. Because of those qualities, water molecules stick to one another, with extraordinary tenacity. It requires an enormous amount of energy to pull them apart (which explains why it requires such a relatively high temperature to change solid water — ice — to liquid water). An enclosed column of water will not break into separate droplets except under enormous tension. In a tree, the water-carrying vessels were initially formed by extremely elongated cells. As they grow, they not only thicken their sides with a substance called lignin, but ultimately break down the dividing wall where they meet, tip to tip, so that they form long continuous tubes, uninterrupted by any divisions. As the cells in a leaf lose water by transpiration, it is replaced by water from the top of the tubes, and the whole water column is pulled upwards. The enormous tensile strength of water prevents it from fragmenting.

Water is also slow to change temperature, and is able to provide physical protection for many forms of life. However, water is a necessity which many people lack. About a third of all people in the world lack clean, safe water. It is a sobering thought that the cost to provide everyone in the world with clean water and safe sanitation would be equivalent to about 1 percent of the money that world governments spend each year on weapons. Now there's a challenge!

Water is a wonderful blessing. Although it is easy to take it for granted, we should never cease from appreciating it, for it is anything but simple. Its abundance, its unique atomic structure, and its versatility all point to the Great Intelligence that has showered us with this liquid far more precious than gold.

Birds of a Feather

There are many reasons to be grateful that you do not live in the 19th century. One of them is the length of time that it took to get dressed each morning. Boots and shoes, coats and suits were all fastened with buttons. Take a look at a very old photograph — people sometimes had to fasten dozens of buttons before they were dressed. An American engineer, Whitcomb Judson, thought he could simplify matters. He invented a new type of fastener. It consisted of a series of clasps that could be opened or closed with a sliding metal guide. He called it his "clasp locker or unlocker for shoes" and

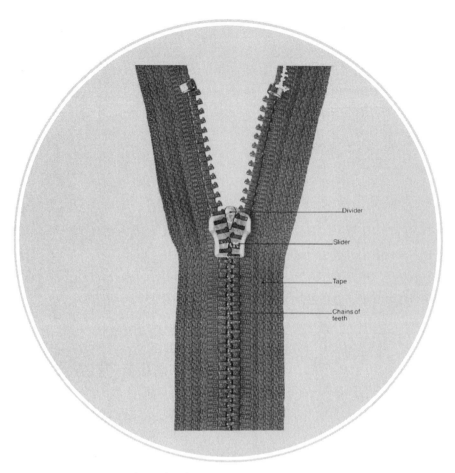

Whitcomb Judson invented the zipper in 1893.

patented it in 1893. Just like its name, the device was somewhat cumbersome, often sticking and equally often popping
open! Over the subsequent 20 years, the device was improved
until it became the modern zipper. The U.S. Navy pioneered
the use of zippers in 1918 when it ordered 10,000 of them to
close windbreakers — and its role as one of the most common
fastening devices was assured.

The mechanism of the zipper is simple. A slider moves up
and down two rows of teeth on tapes, locking and unlocking
them. The teeth on each strip are staggered so that they can
dovetail together. They have a projection on one side and a
hollow on the other, so that when they are meshed together,

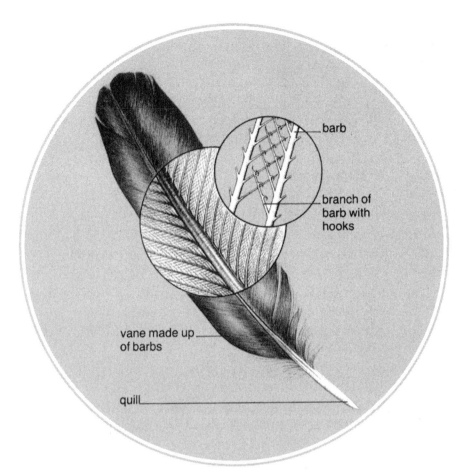

But who invented the feather?

the projections fit into the hollows. The name zipper? It was taken from the hissing sound the device makes when the slider is pulled quickly up and down. Simple yet effective. Yet, for all its effectiveness, the zipper has its limitations. If it gets stuck, as it sometimes does, it cannot free itself. If it becomes clogged with dirt, it cannot clean itself. It is incapable of changing color, it does not grow longer, nor can the zipper send messages. It cannot even help you hide from your enemies! May we introduce to you the humble feather, which can do everything a zipper can do, only much better.

The feather is unique to the bird. There is no animal, reptile or mammal that possesses this unique creation. Keen observers of the natural world will have noticed that birds can fly. A bird does not have to be diminutive to fly — even large birds like eagles or plump birds like partridges can become airborne. (The wandering albatross is the biggest with a huge wingspan of more than 11 feet.) Their skeletons are specially designed for flying, including lightweight bones with special attachment sites for flight muscles. Many bones are hollow, supported by struts of bone for strength. The breastbone is drawn out into a flattened keel, with flight muscles attached. They have a rigid structure for transmitting the forces of flight to the rest of the body. Air sacs extend from the lungs in order to increase the bird's buoyancy. There really is no difference whatsoever between the specialized design of an airplane (which is the result of an enormous investment of millions of dollars, energy and intelligence) and the characteristic features of the bird which pops out of an egg, the product of an enormous Intelligence. And then there are feathers.

Feathers provide a large, strong surface area, and weigh very little. Feathers enable a bird to fly and help it maintain a constant body temperature. They do this by trapping a layer of air against the skin. Air is a poor conductor of heat, so this layer of air holds heat inside the body. (Emperor penguins are the toughest of all the animals in Antarctica. They survive months of almost total darkness, temperatures that can drop to 40 degrees below 0, and the fiercest winds and blizzards on earth. How do they survive? Fat and feathers. They have a thick layer of blubber which protects them from the cold and is a store of energy. Their feathers are packed tightly together, and fit over one another to make a coat that is four feathers thick.) Feathers also provide coloring that helps the bird both to hide from its enemies and to attract a mate.

Although feathers are remarkably durable, they gradually wear out. Since it is not possible to go shopping for a new set, birds simply (!) shed the old ones and grow a new set at least once a year. But now we have a problem. Imagine that you gave your car in for service and repair. How would you get from place to place in the interim? The bird needs its large primary feathers, the ones that are attached to the wings, for flying. If they were all to fall out simultaneously, how would our bird fly? Have no fear. In a planned system, everything is taken care of. Flight feathers are shed and replaced in a specific order that allows a bird to continue flying while molting (feather change) takes place.

At first sight, a feather looks simple. Closer investigation proves that it is anything but. Running down the center is the quill. This central shaft is hollow up to about two thirds of its length (giving it both strength and lightness). Beyond this point, it becomes solid to increase its strength at the thinner end. The base of the quill is rooted in the skin. If it was up to you, how would you attach a feather into skin? Just stick it in and hope for the best? In the created world, nothing at all is simple, and everything is clever. Each feather is in fact attached to a muscle so that the feather can be moved. When an airplane manipulates its rudder, elevators and ailerons in order to climb, descend or turn (using mechanical and electronic technology), it is doing nothing else but copying the capabilities of the humble but ultrasophisticated bird. Growing out from the central shaft are hundreds of barbs, which make up the web of the feather. Each barb in turn carries hundreds of tiny filaments, called barbules, and these are equipped with minute hooks which interlock with the adjacent row of barbules. This unique arrangement gives the vane (feathered part of the quill) both strength and flexibility. A sudden blow to the vane is more likely to separate the hooks from neighboring barbs than to tear or break the feather. The whole structure works much like a zipper. If the web splits as a result of the hooks becoming separated, the bird simply draws the feather through its beak a few times and the condition of the vane is restored.

If the sophisticated structure would have ended there — *dayeinu* — it would have sufficed to convince us of the presence of a Higher Intelligence. But it does not. In rainy weather, you and I protect ourselves by putting on a raincoat.

If the feathers of a bird became waterlogged and heavy, the bird would have as much chance of flying as a hippopotamus. How then do birds protect their precious feathers from the elements? The answer is oil. Water tends to run straight off an oily surface without wetting it. Not surprisingly, birds have been equipped with their own oil pump! When preening, a bird spreads oil onto its feathers from the preen gland on its rump. Some birds have special powder puffs which they use to groom their feathers. Herons, who live in marshland, have no less than five powder puffs, one on the chest and two on each thigh. They clean off fish slime by rubbing their feathers through the powder. A comb on one of their claws removes the clogged powder, and leaves the feathers clean and tidy. It is nothing less amazing than if coal miners grew an electric lamp from their foreheads to enable them to see in the dark!

Birds have several different types of feather, each with a different function. Long wing feathers are used for flying, and downy feathers insulate the body. The filoflumes, the tiny, hairlike feathers that are left behind when a bird is plucked, provide the bird with a flight-monitoring system. Each filoflume has a long shaft (relative to its size) with a tuft of soft barbs at the tip. It is always situated next to a large feather, and it is believed that it senses the movements of the larger feathers, and triggers nerves that send signals to the bird's brain with regard to air speed, wind direction, buffeting and any other air movements that might affect its flight. And you thought that feathers just made birds look pretty?

The color of a bird's feathers (plumage) can play a vital part in its search for food, and its very survival. Terns and many other fish-eating sea birds have white underparts. Unsuspecting fish cannot see them against the bright sky, enabling the terns to feed freely. Brent geese migrate in flocks from Siberia to Europe. To make sure they keep together and do not lose sight of one another, the birds have a white rump that is easily seen from behind in flight. Another species of birds, the ptarmigan, lives in the Arctic and on high mountains. To provide year-round camouflage, its plumage changes color with the seasons. In spring it is mottled brown to blend with plants; in autumn it is grey to look like rocks; and in winter it turns white to match the snow. Even birds need to find *shidduchim.* The color of their feathers can help here too. The red bishop of the African plains is pale brown for most of the year. To find a mate, his plumage changes to black and red, and he fluffs out his feathers making him look like a brilliantly colored ball. He then bounces over the plains in a strange, bounding flight.

Presumably, the future Mrs. Red Bishop is impressed, and they live happily ever after.

The question is, of course: How do you plan the color of your feathers? Who told the terns the secret of white undersides? Who told the red bishop that those found on the other side of the *mechitzah* are fond of red — and what is the mechanism for changing color? The questions abound, but all have one answer. The more details that are uncovered about feathers (as in every aspect of the created world) the more one discovers the limitless Intelligence that created everything.

Vaya'ar Elokim es kol asher asah vehinei tov meod.

The Virtuoso

Some mothers are ambitious. Not necessarily for themselves, you understand, but for their children. Inspired by a dream of their offspring achieving international fame and renown, the little cherubs have to suffer hours of lessons and practice learning to play the piano or violin. Suffer is the appropriate word. While Junior mercilessly scrapes the horse-hair over the catgut (violin bow over the strings), strongly resembling the nightmarish nocturnal wailings of anguished pussycats, or crashes along the keyboard like a runaway rhinoceros, mother stands enraptured, a faraway look in her eyes, enveloped in pleasure.

There is no doubt, however, that a select few do make the grade. Whether the Paganinis and the Menuhins of this world had ambitious mothers, or were simply gifted with a natural talent, is, in the final analysis, immaterial. The virtuosos in our midst play their instruments with flair and expertise, and give many people much pleasure in the process. No one would claim that the skill of a polished musician was achieved without practice. Even the simplest instrument — flute, bagpipes or drum — requires dedication and tenacity — as well as inherent talent, to be played effectively. Great skill does not happen by itself. What is true of humans applies equally to all creatures.

If you go into the woods tonight, you're likely to find a bat. These nocturnal flyers utilize tremendous skill both navigating, and finding their supper. Some bats have such sensitive hearing that they can detect the sound of an insect's wing flutters. Moths fly as silently as flitting shadows. You and I would never ever hear them. But the bat has been gifted with exceptionally sensitive hearing. Not only that, but they use an ultrasophisticated system known as echolocation to locate their victims. They send out high-pitched shrieks at regular intervals and listen for the echoes that bounce off the insect's body. By this means they can pinpoint its position, and how far away it is. Even these bare facts sound complicated enough to be impressive. The details are even more impressive.

All sound has a pitch. A high note is said to have a high pitch, and conversely a low note has a lower pitch. Sound travels in waves, the length of a wave being determined by the pitch of the sound. The higher the sound, the shorter its wavelength, and therefore the smaller the surface its echo can reveal. We can hear some bat sounds, particularly when we are young and our hearing is sharp, but those squeaks are nothing more than the bat saying hello. The squeaks, or clicks that they emit for navigation, are so high pitched that they are ultrasonic, far beyond the range of any human ear.

Some are so high that they enable their makers to detect the presence of a wire no thicker than a human hair.

Then you have the intensity of the sound. The louder it is, the more distant the object it can detect. Bats produce clicks, which, if translated into frequencies that we can hear, would sound as loud as a pneumatic drill. This, however, causes a major complication. It is so loud that were the bats to hear it, their hypersensitive ears, tuned to detect the faintest of echoes (the almost silent beatings of a moth's wings), would be seriously overloaded. This problem is dealt with by a muscle in the bat's middle ear, attached to one of the trio of tiny bones that transmits the vibrations of the eardrum to the hearing organ in the skull that converts them into electrical stimuli. As each click is made, this muscle pulls aside the bone so that the eardrum is momentarily disconnected. It is then replaced in time to receive the echo. This incredible feat is performed more than a hundred times a second, in perfect synchrony with the clicks of the calls.

It is worth dwelling on this amazing capability for a moment. If you would see a pianist's fingers striking the keys at the rate of 100 strikes per second, you would be witnessing the superhuman. See how many times you can tap your fingers on the table in the space of one second! If those 100 notes would be in perfect harmony, your amazement would know no bounds. Here is a little creature, that has never taken lessons and never learned anything, activating and deactivating a single muscle (which itself involves electrical and chemical processes of enormous complexity) in the middle of its head, 100 times every second. And it has to be done in perfect synchronization with the sounds which it emits from its vocal cords, otherwise the whole system would be useless. And it works perfectly! Anyone who knows anything about the airplanes of the first World War, and is impressed by the synchronization of the machine gun that could fire its bullets through the whirling propeller without ripping it to shreds, can be equally impressed by the engineering techniques demonstrated by the humble, unassuming bat.

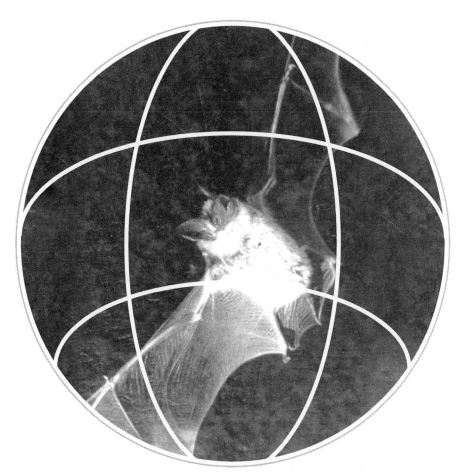

The bat that flies at night – the original radar machine.

Don't for a minute imagine that 100 clicks a second is the world record! The faster the clicks are emitted, the more up-to-date information the bat will receive as it negotiates the obstacles in the cave and dodges through the branches and creepers of the night forest. Some bats can send out a stream of 200 clicks in a single second, each lasting only a thousandth of a second, and spaced sufficiently from the other to allow each echo to be heard. Now that is virtuosity!

The sophistication goes even further. The horseshoe bat (named because of the unique shape of its nose) emits sounds through its nose, the calls being focused into a narrow beam by a formation of flesh around the nose. Unlike other bats, these bats emit their calls at a constant pitch. By turning its head to scan from side to side, a hunting horseshoe bat can tell not only the position of an insect by echolocation, but also the direction in which it is flying. It can also do this because of the Doppler effect. This is a phenomenon named after C.J. Doppler, a 19th-century Austrian physicist who discovered it. An obvious demonstration of this effect occurs to a pedestrian as a police car with siren wailing goes by. The siren's notes seem to be higher as the car approaches and lower as it speeds away. This is because, although the notes have not changed pitch, as the car gets closer, the sound waves have less distance to travel, so their frequency per second increases, and as the frequency increases, so does the pitch. As the car speeds away, the sound waves returning have further to travel, so their frequency decreases as does the pitch.

Enter Mr. Bat! A horseshoe bat, who has never heard of Herr Doppler, or a country called Austria, compares the pitch of the echoes from a flying insect with the pitch of the constant frequency signals it sent out. An echo of lower pitch than the signal means that the insect is moving away. An echo of higher pitch means that the insect is moving closer. In this way, the bat tracks the insect's flight path.

There is another dark world where animals use sonar to find their way around. Many great rivers — the Ganges and the Indus, the Amazon and the Yangtze — are so muddy that the animals swimming in them cannot see more than a few inches ahead. A dolphin is able to produce sonar clicks by forcing air through special passages and sinuses in its head. These are focused into a beam by an oval, fat-packed organ — the melon — which forms a bulge on the dolphin's forehead. This is, in effect, a sound lens and it produces a sonic searchlight with which the animal scans the water ahead of it. An interesting feature of this apparatus is that the beam of sound that is emitted from the forehead fans out at an angle of 9 degrees. If the angle were narrower, and the beam any more intense, the sound energy would turn to heat! The beam enables a dolphin to find and identify small objects at great distances. A bottlenose dolphin can locate a tangerine-sized ball from 124 yards away. It can distinguish between plates of copper and of aluminum which have been painted the same color, and can tell a hollow tube from a solid one.

The speed with which a dolphin produces clicks makes the bat seem slothlike by comparison. The clicks are emitted at a rate of 700 per second, much too fast for the analytical capability of the human ear and brain. At 20-30 clicks a second, our ears fuse the sounds together, so to us the echolocation clicks that can be heard sound like the squeaks of a rusty hinge. But the dolphin can distinguish each tiny item of sound. Returning echoes inform it about the structure of the object that it is investigating, and whether it is animate or inanimate. The returning echoes, after bouncing off a target, do not enter the dolphin's ear canal, but are picked up instead by the teeth of its lower jaw — perhaps one reason why dolphins' mouths are perpetually open in a characteristic half-smile. The teeth absorb the sound vibrations and transfer them to the thin bone of the jaw. From there, they travel along the jaw to the middle ear via a channel of fatty tissue.

So there you are. Next time you are out on a dark night, and cannot find your way home, just start clicking. What you could never teach yourself to do in a thousand years, the bats and dolphins of this world have been doing effortlessly and efficiently since they were created. Endowed with such consummate skill and equipped with such sophisticated machinery, they are indeed the virtuosos of creation — fitting testimony to the limitless wisdom of their Creator.

Jet Propelled

Occasionally, laws of physics can be illustrated by interesting stories. Once upon a time, a recently married couple went on an outing during their summer vacation. Not possessing a car, they took a bus to a picturesque little town through which a wide river gently meandered. The young couple decided to rent a rowboat, to enjoy a serene half-hour on the river. With the oars in the hands of the young man, the boat fairly skimmed along the surface. An idyllic picture, you might think. It was, until the boat grounded in the shallow waters near the riverbank. The young man, whose navigational experience was minimal, gallantly jumped onto the riverbank, and with his feet firmly implanted against the bank, began to push the boat outwards with his two hands. Slowly, the boat began to move, and inexorably, as the distance between the boat and the river bank increased, so did the angle of tilt of the young man. At a certain point, in the struggle between the forces of gravity and the attachment to the boat, victory was claimed by gravity, and with a resounding splash the young man fell headlong into the river. His young wife, with all the sympathy and compassion that you would expect from a newlywed, burst into uncontrollable laughter!

As the young man disconsolately squelched his way back to the bus, he could have comforted himself in the knowledge that he had dramatically demonstrated the second Newtonian law of motion; that every action has an equal and opposite reaction. On the basis of this law, if you want to project yourself forward in a swimming pool, you place your foot on the side of the pool and push backwards. Much the same effect is caused when a fireman holds the nozzle of a hose. He feels a strong force pushing him backwards in the opposite direction to that in which he is squirting water, because the jet of water reacts, or pushes, against the nozzle. It is important to note that the thrust has nothing to do with the jet pushing against the surrounding air (or water) after it leaves the nozzle. The fireman would feel the same force pushing him backwards if he were standing on a planet with no atmosphere at all, where there would be no air for the jet of water to push against.

When an aircraft or boat is driven forwards by causing it to squirt a jet of air or water backwards, it is said to be jet propelled. Strictly speaking, all kinds of aircraft and ships are jet propelled, because they all throw jets of air or water backwards in order to move, usually by means of a propeller. The expression "jet propulsion" is generally used where the propeller is not to be seen. The jet engine works when fuel is burned in the heart of an engine, exhaust gases stream out of the back, and so the engine moves forward. We take for granted fast, regular flights connecting all the world's major cities, powered by jet engines. We might be forgiven for thinking that jet propulsion is a relatively modern invention ...

Until we realize that all the knowledge and applied wisdom mentioned above has been utilized by birds and fish ever since they were created. Take a simple example: Unlike most shellfish, such as cockles and mussels, queen scallops do not simply rely on their hard shells for protection. As soon as a queen scallop is aware of the approach of a predatory starfish, it claps its hinged shell vigorously and repeatedly, forcing out jets of water that propel it away from the starfish, The slow-moving starfish is unable to match this burst of speed and will go in search of a less mobile meal. Now scallop shells are most elegant, and have been used as ornaments for centuries. There are those (non-Jewish) who consume the edible part of the scallop, the large white muscle of the creature living inside the pair of shells. However, without wishing to offend, scallops are not known for their intelligence. How then did the scallop master the theory and techniques, let alone acquire the equipment, of jet propulsion? The answer is one word: Creation.

Deep down in the great oceans lives the squid. These animals can grow to quite a size, and a fully grown 60-feet long giant squid has eyes the size of footballs. Interestingly enough, a deep-water squid can use polarized light — a rare ability which allows it to make out the shape of its quarry extremely clearly, even in low-light conditions. Combined with its speed and natural aggression, this facility makes it a highly efficient hunter. Keep clear if you can! Now if you would have a boat, 60-feet long, it would require an engine of considerable power to propel it through the water. How then does the giant squid manage? A squid draws water into its mantle, and expels it through a pair of nozzles, situated adjacent to its large eyes. This is jet propulsion that is so powerful that it sometimes rockets the creature above the surface. Generally, a squid moves backwards, but it can in-

Jet-propelled sophistication, but nowhere as sophisticated as the original

stantly change direction by swiveling its nozzles, rather as a vertical takeoff aircraft alters the direction of its jets. Side fins, like the planes of a submarine, adjust the angles of ascent and descent. Sophistication beyond belief, a sure sign of intelligence, is just part and parcel of the squid's design. The squid, oblivious to this discussion, just jet-propels along as he has always done, without even knowing whether "sophistication" is spelled with an "f" or "ph."

It should never be imagined that size alone is a criterion for sophisticated capabilities or equipment. From the greatest to the most humble, the common denominator is the same — endless complexity which could never have come about with having been created. Human beings tend to have a rather exalted opinion of themselves, and look down at "lower life forms" as primitive. However, if these life forms could talk, they would have plenty to say for themselves. In a recently published book, *Darwin's Black Box — the Biochemical Challenge to Evolution*, by Michael J. Behe, the author examines the workings of the smallest particle of living material — the cell. Cells come in all shapes and sizes, and although they are tiny, they are anything but simple. There are even cells that swim, using a *cilium*. A cilium is a structure that, simply put, looks like a hair and lashes like a whip. If a cell with a cilium is free to move about in a liquid, the cilium moves the cell much as an oar moves a boat. If the cell is stuck in the middle of a sheet of other cells, the beating cilium moves liquid over the surface of the stationary cell. For example, the stationary cells that line the breathing tract each have several hundred cilia. The large number of cilia beat in synchrony, much like the oars handled by slaves on a Roman galley, to push mucus up to the throat for expulsion. The action removes small foreign particles — like soot — that are accidentally inhaled and become stuck in the mucus.

So here you have a cell that swims. It propels itself along, just like your squid. Simple? — anything but. Mechanical examples of swimming systems are easy to find. Take a wind-up fish that wiggles its tail, propelling itself through the bathtub. The tail of the toy fish is the paddle surface, the wound spring is the energy source, and a connecting rod transmits the energy. If any one of the components — the paddle, motor, or connector — is missing, then the fish goes nowhere. A swimming system without a paddle, motor or connector is fatally incomplete. Because the swimming system needs several parts to work, and each is essential, it is impossible for it to have developed gradually. Transfer the swimming requirements from your toy fish to a boat, and the list of minimal requirements increases. A paddle is necessary, but if its surface is too small, a boat may not move significantly in a required amount of time. Conversely, if the paddle surface is too large, the connector or motor might strain and break when moving. The motor must be strong enough to move the paddle. It must be regulated to an appropriate speed. Too slow, the boat would get nowhere. Too fast, and the connector or the paddle might break.

Once upon a time, there were microscopes that used light to illuminate the subject. Light microscopes showed thin hairs on some cells. The discovery of the complex Lilliputian details of the cilia had to wait for the discovery of the electron microscope, which revealed that the cilium is a structure no less complex, and considerably more sophisticated than the mechanism that propels the most modern ship. The tiny cilium cell has a motor, connectors and paddles. The details involve complexity beyond belief. And it works. All of its parts are required to perform one function — motion. Just as your motorboat will not work unless all of its constituent parts are present, neither will the ciliary cell. It is impossible for it to have developed. It was designed to work, it does work, and it had a Designer!

From large to small, from squid to scallop to cell, the story is repeated. Systems of advanced sophistication, irreducibly complex, that efficiently and eloquently propel the human mind to recognize the Hand of Hashem in every living thing.

Canned fruit is the ultimate convenience food. Let there be 12 inches of snow outside; you can be eating your canned cherries as if it were the middle of summer. Reach for a can of bean soup at any time of the day or night, and a nourishing meal can be on your table within five minutes. It was not always so easy. In the 1790s, the armies of Napoleon Bonaparte were marching across Europe. It was often difficult for them to obtain food, and in 1795 Napoleon offered a prize of 12,000 francs for a method of preserving food. A Paris confectioner and baker, Monsieur Nicolas Appert, read about the prize.

Scientists at this time knew nothing about why food decayed, so Appert had to work by trial and error. After 14 years of work, he made an important discovery. Liquid foods like stews and small fruit were preserved if he sealed them inside wine bottles and heated the bottles in boiling water. The French army liked his preserved food, and Monsieur Appert won the prize together with a contract to supply the army with bottled soup and vegetables. His work was taken up by others, who used metal cans instead of breakable bottles, and the canning industry was born.

Imagine that you were a cherry safely ensconced inside your can. Realizing that your purpose in life was to give nourishment and pleasure to human beings, there is nothing that you would like more than to exit from your tin tomb and be eaten. Problem. Did Monsieur Appert and his friends remember to invent the can opener together with the can? And even so, it is the humans who are in possession of the can opener, not the cherry. How will you, the cherry, escape? Now if you were simply a fruit or vegetable, the consequences of remaining locked inside the can forever would be inconsequential. But what would happen if you were a little unborn creature locked inside an egg? In order for your species to continue, you must find a method of exiting from your egg! If the egg was tough and leathery, as many eggs are, the problem would be exacerbated. What to do!

Snake eggs indeed have a strong shell. But they also have a can opener. To cut their way out of the eggshell, snake embryos are supplied with a special implement, an egg tooth, that curves forwards from the center of the upper lip. The egg tooth is usually flat and very sharp; the infant snake uses it like a saw, waving its head from side to side until it cuts a slit in the shell. Once the young snake is out of its nursery, the egg tooth soon falls off. Think for a moment. It is futile to ask which came first, the thick, leathery protective eggshell or the toothy can opener. It is futile because it is clear that one without the other would not work. They must have come into existence simultaneously. To design a protective fortress in which creatures are not only safely preserved, but can actually develop, is an act of ingenuity. To provide the creatures with an integral disposable exit mechanism is ingenuity compounded with foresight. A mighty wisdom is indicated. The snake's can opener is but one example of the planning and wisdom incorporated in the egg's design. There are many others.

Although all birds' eggs are oval, there are significant differences between those laid by various species. There is a bird called the guillemot. This not-so-little bird breeds on sea-facing cliffs, and lays a single egg on the bare rock. If the egg would roll just two inches, it would disappear over the ledge. Fortunately, its egg is tapered sharply at each end, so that it rolls in tight circles. It has the precise shape to prevent its falling off. To give it added protection, the shell is specially thickened at each end.

There is a bird called the fairy tern, that exercises some of the most alarming nesting habits imaginable; but the bird survives. It balances its eggs on the bare branches of trees, or on stark rock ledges which are hardly bigger than the egg itself. The female tern selects the place on which it will deposit its single egg with the exactness of a darts player, placing the egg on it with an audible click. And there, without budging, it stays. Realize the danger — here lies an egg, with no tangible clamp, clip or adhesive material to bond it to the selected spot. If the egg moved as much as three eighths of an inch on its bare branch, it would fall off and smash. That it remains safely in place is wonder enough. But it has to be born too! Both parent terns sit on their egg in turn, one on duty while the other feeds at sea. When the chick hatches, it stays stock still, never moving from the spot until it is ready to fly, about five weeks later. Baby tern is born with extra long claws to give it a grip on its inhospitable perch. Fortunate!

Like many other birds, the hen pheasant does not lay all her eggs at once. Instead, she gradually builds up her complete clutch. Pheasants lay up to 20 eggs — one every day or

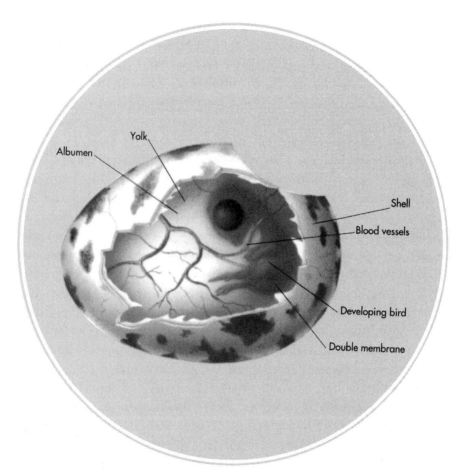

The chick's egg — safest home in the world

so. But not until she has laid the complete complement does the hen start incubating. This is because the the survival of the chicks depends on them all hatching at the same time. Only a day or two after they hatch, their mother leads them away from the nest to look for food. Any little one that had not yet hatched would be unable to follow. It is a fact that if you left an egg lying around in your kitchen for a week or so, it might not retain its freshness. In the case of the hen pheasant, not only does it not go bad, it can be successfully incubated to form a viable life. Experiments have shown that if a clutch of pheasant eggs is put under a brooding hen, and another clutch is added 12 hours later, all the chicks will still hatch at the same time. Developing chicks signal to each other by peeping and tapping to ensure that they all hatch simultaneously. Mother hen pheasant constantly rolls her eggs over, a measure that prevents the membranes from sticking to the shells. Such wisdom in a creature that does not even know how to spell wisdom!

People say that you cannot help when you were born. That might be true of humans, but in the animal world there are examples of creatures that demonstrate remarkable skills in deciding the precise moment to enter the world. Down in Australia, there are what the locals call *billabongs*. Billabongs are stagnant pools, and are the chosen habitat for the pig-nosed turtle (not the most complementary of names!). In the dry season, the female turtles emerge to dig holes in the sandy banks, high above the water line, and in its hole each lays about a dozen or so eggs. These develop safely in the warm sand until ready to hatch, about 10 weeks later. If the rainy season has begun and the sand is wet, the young turtles break out of their leathery shells immediately and slip down into the water below, as happy as you like. Otherwise, they wait patiently for the rains to arrive, lapsing in the meanwhile into a torpor in which they need no food and hardly any air. The precise mechanism by which the unborn turtle knows what the weather is like outside its unbroken shell is unknown, as is the mechanism which acts to freeze its development. It is certainly not simple, and could not have happened by chance ...

Any more than its relative, another freshwater turtle — the painted turtle — which also delays its arrival into the active world. These turtles survive the cold of southern Canada in the same way as many of its mammals — by hibernating. Female painted turtles nest in midsummer in south-facing banks (to gain maximum heat.) There they lay their eggs, and 12 weeks later, the youngsters hatch. But by this time, winter is fast approaching, so the young turtles stay where they are until spring. During the winter, they too go into a torpor, eating nothing and barely moving. Their bodies contain a natural antifreeze that enables them to survive for long periods when the temperature in the nest drops below freezing. "Natural antifreeze" — now that sounds interesting. This coming winter, if you live in a location where the temperature drops below zero, and you are a car owner, have no fear. Simply whisper in your car's ear (located just below the gas cap) and ask it to develop its own antifreeze overnight to prevent the radiator from freezing. If the painted turtle can do it, why not your car? Wait a moment, isn't antifreeze a modern invention? If so, how did the turtle discover the secret? How indeed!

There is another example of birds demonstrating wisdom far beyond their natural intelligence — the manner in which they keep their eggs cool. Most eggs can survive for a short time if their temperature drops from the normal 98 degrees Fahrenheit to as low as 77 degrees Fahrenheit. But a slight rise in their temperature to 102 degrees Fahrenheit for the same length of time is fatal. For birds nesting in the tropics, keeping their eggs cool is a continual battle. Even though no one has ever told them the importance of keeping their eggs cool, they do it, and they do it well. There are the plovers of the East African plains whose nests are in the open air, and who stand over their eggs with wings spread out to shade them from the sun. You have the tropical herons who coat their eggs with their own droppings to maintain their temperature. This acts like a cool bag — the outside may become hot, but the contents remain cool. Shading works well enough if the eggs are exposed only to direct sunlight, but if the air temperature around them is too high, different tactics are necessary. The Australian black-necked stork carries water in its beak to spray over the eggs!

Just like the invention of canned food, life-saving mechanisms are not accidental, but a demonstration of the greatest intelligence. The Greatest Intelligence of all!

Ma rabu maasecha Hashem.

Hydraulic Wisdom

No word is more evocative than "home." Take the toughest soldier overseas on a tour of duty, the strongest athlete around the world on his grand tour, mention the word "home" and they will become misty eyed. Home is where you are accepted, home is where you feel welcome, home is the place where you can be yourself.

A home is also a house, and houses have to be built. It used to be fairly simple (and still is) to build a structure of wood and clay, with a roof constructed of thatch, or reeds. An Eskimo can sculpt his igloo with little more than a knife, and a native in Africa can assemble his round hut of mud, branches and grass in no time at all. If, however, you have to dig foundations, and erect an edifice of brick, concrete and glass many floors high, that is an entirely different question. Especially if before you begin your construction, you have to demolish an existing building. Imagine how difficult it was before the age of modern machinery. Knocking down a house is not that difficult, but filling cart after cart with rubble and clearing the site must have been both arduous and time consuming. And then digging the trenches for the foundations — just imagine hammering through rocky substrata with nothing more sophisticated than human muscle holding a shovel!

Enter the mechanical digger. This tough fellow, with his impressive array of accessories, is indispensable to any building site. Buildings are knocked to the ground with swinging extended hammers, huge caterpillar treads allow the mechanical monsters to crawl up the steepest incline, clawing at the mountain of rubble and tossing tons of stone and brick into the waiting line of heavy trucks as easily as a child throws a rubber ball. Within days the site is cleared, allowing the extending arms of the digger to probe deep into the clinging earth, cutting long and straight excavations for the new foundations. The whole complex operation can be carried out without one human finger becoming soiled.

How do these mechanical grabs — powerful yet graceful — work? What force powers their herculean feats of strength? The answer is a single word: fluid. The branch of physics that studies the behavior of liquids is called hydraulics (from two Greek words, meaning "water" and "pipe"). Since water, as all liquids, cannot be compressed (no matter how hard you try, you just cannot squeeze two pints into a pint jar), fluids have the capability to exert enormous force. It is the pressure from water or some other fluid that supplies the power that runs hydraulic machines. For example: A simple hydraulic press consists of a cylinder that contains two pistons, one smaller than the other. The cylinder is filled with a fluid. A force applied to the smaller piston is transferred through the fluid to the larger piston. The force increases in direct proportion to the ratio of the area of the larger piston to the area of the smaller piston. Car brakes operate on this principle. Pressure applied to the brake pedal is transmitted through a liquid to brake shoes, which press against the car's wheels. Our familiar bulldozer, master builder and demolisher, is worked in much the same way, by hydraulic jacks to which pressure from an engine-driven pump is admitted through a control valve operated by a driver.

A new and brilliant innovation? The invention of the century? Not quite. There are many animals, among them worms and slugs that depend on hydraulics to move around. They move, not by the working of muscles on joints, but by the interaction of muscles and fluid power. An earthworm, for example, is a muscular fluid-filled tube. As the fluids cannot be compressed, contracting its muscles causes a worm to stretch and push its sharp end into the soil. When the muscles are relaxed the worm gets shorter and fatter until the next muscular pressure against the fluids makes it advance once more. By tensing or relaxing its muscles, a worm can turn in any direction, its tube made both constant and flexible by the counterpressure of its hydraulic system. The worm is not an intelligent creature, and lacks any ability to ponder its place in the world, let alone consider the most effective and efficient method to crawl around. If it had any such ability, it probably would have grown wings and flown — it's so much quicker! If the humble worm has been equipped with a sophisticated hydraulic system, it must have been designed and fitted out by an Intelligence outside of itself.

If you are looking for something even less intelligent than the lowly worm, there is indeed a suitable candidate. The creature in question lives on the sea bed, has five arms (arranged in starlike formation) and hundreds of legs. It is the famous starfish. The starfish is remarkable. It has no brain of any description. Motionless, seeming inert as a rock, the starfish lies with extended rigid arms upon the ocean floor.

A mechanical digger — indispensable to all building sites

Currents of water lift its spiny body and shift and tumble it. For hour after hour, the starfish may float and drift, with no evidence that there is any life inside it or controlling it. But sooner or later, the mute pentagon makes a tiny stir. Slowly, slower than the snail, it begins walking. And when it does so, it uses a hydraulic system that would put the most sophisticated bulldozer to shame.

On the starfish's back, near its center, there is a circular structure which acts like a sieve. Through this device, the starfish begins to suck in sea water. Via intricate canals, the water courses through its body and, by means of a series of interior valves and reservoirs, is carried out to the extremities of the five radial arms. (There is nothing that demonstrates design as clearly as a valve. Think of your central-heating system!) Along all the arms' undersides, which are deeply grooved from their tips to the central orifice which is the starfish's mouth, there are thousands of little feet. They are about three quarters of an inch long, and each of them terminates in a little suction pad. Each of the thousands of feet is hollow, and they move in perfect coordination. As perfectly as the hundreds of water taps in a large hotel are all connected in a single coordinated system, so all the starfish's many feet are plumbed into a muscular system powered by water. It is a locomotion achieved, quite literally, by the starfish's act of drinking.

In the water-vascular system of the starfish, the indrawn water flows out into the tube feet, filling them. As each water-filled foot is pressed against the ocean floor, the starfish rhythmically draws the water out from it again, and thus creates a tiny suction tube. Alternately fastening the tube feet and withdrawing them (all perfectly timed and coordinated), the starfish goes creeping through the water. Now, as it makes its way, it keeps thrusting out a special tube foot, suckerless, at the tip of each of its arms — tapping and reaching and feeling with these instruments in groping investigation which is its substitute for vision.

It is worthwhile hearing how this fascinating creature eats, for it is in its amazing eating habits that we see the strength of its hydraulic power. The starfish is hungry. When it comes across a clam or oyster, it has found its prey. Slowly, cumbersomely, the starfish creeps up on top of its prey, and surrounds it, its five arms bent over the shell like an imprisoning cage. It then begins to apply its sucker feet; foot after foot fasten with suction tightness to one side of the victim's two-part shell, foot after foot apply to the other. When at last the tremendous grip has been fully arranged, the starfish begins to pull. It pulls with the enormous strength of steadiness, the steadiness with which a growing plant splits a rock. Constantly and relentlessly it pulls. No clam or oyster has muscles strong enough to hold its shell closed indefinitely against such force. It pulls for hours on end if need be until finally the tightly shut shell flies open. (What happens next is not for the squeamish. Out of the starfish's mouth comes its stomach, which it inserts into the open shell, and pours out digestive juices. Slowly but surely, the starfish digests every edible fragment of the oyster or clam, draws its stomach back into its mouth, and is ready to move on, with its water-driven feet, to the next course.)

The hydraulic system operated by the starfish, and also by a similar creature called the sea urchin, not only enables them to walk, grip and exert pressure. It is used also to transport dissolved gases, food and waste products.

The abilities of these humble creatures is breathtaking. All the more because they themselves are mindless and as oblivious to the physical forces of this world as pieces of rock. Yet they demonstrate an intricacy of construction and technical expertise which is far beyond our own ability to comprehend. We are impressed, and rightly so, when we witness the skill and construction of our mechanical diggers. The admiration that we express for the inventors and designers of the hydraulic tools that are so much a part of modern life is genuine and heartfelt. By understanding the wisdom of our modern appliances we begin to gain an inkling into the vast Intelligence that has designed and constructed the wonderful world in which we live.

Food for Thought

T he story goes that once there was an East European king who, poor fellow, was suffering from insomnia. Neither potions nor lotions, neither pills nor lullabies could induce him to sleep.

Fortunately, the king employed a Jewish adviser who was upset at his master's discomfort, and thought that he had the answer. "Your Majesty," said the *Yid*, "I think I can help you. Every Saturday, which, as you know, is my day off, I eat a delicious *cholent*. It's heavy, stodgy and rich. Immediately after the meal, I take a volume of the Talmud, sit in the armchair and open the large book. Within two minutes

I'm asleep. Every week — guaranteed. If you would consent to try it, I am sure it would work." The king was desperate. He agreed. The adviser's adviser'tzen prepared a *cholent* fit for a king, and the king ate not one plate, but two! He then sat in an armchair; the adviser handed him a volume of the Talmud, and tiptoed quietly out of the room, anticipating the contented snores. Half an hour later, the king roared for his adviser. The disgruntled king was sitting, wide awake. "Why hasn't it worked?" growled the king. "Oh, your Majesty — of course it didn't work — you're holding the book upside down!"

There is no doubt that *cholent* is famous for its sleep-inducing qualities. (There is a righteous woman who refuses to give her equally righteous husband *cholent* because she wants him to learn on Shabbos afternoon!) Left-over *cholent* can also be sold to the building trade for use as quick-setting cement. There is no doubt that apart from *cholent*, there are numerous examples of foods that have remarkable qualities, many of which are relatively unrecognized. It is perfectly logical that in a created world, designed by the Greatest Intelligence, each and every fruit and plant, in the vast variety of plant life that exists, should be of some benefit to something. "Nothing that Hashem created in His world has been created needlessly" (*Shabbos* 77b).

Modern man has been conditioned to consider the breathtaking advance of the pharmaceutical industry as one of the great benefits of this century. There is much to be grateful for in that area, as the magic bullets concocted in the laboratory are used in the fight against ailments large and small. But we are advancing yet further. Many scientists are increasingly engaged in a search for a far different treasure of drugs that were created on this planet together with mankind. These drugs come from other living creatures and plants. They are the stuff we, often without thought, put into our mouths, every day. These substances, too, are miraculous — awesome in their ability to affect our well-being. Food can enhance health and vigor, it can stimulate the brain and elevate our spirits. Food can trigger headaches and asthma attacks, as well as prevent them. Food can cure diarrhea in infants and constipation in the elderly. Food can alter immunity, chasing away common colds and hay fever. For those interested in appreciating the wonderful world created by Hashem *Yisbarach*, it is worthwhile looking at the amazing qualities embodied by different foods. A recent book, *Food — Your Miracle Medicine* by Jean Harper (published by Simon & Schuster), contains a wealth of material in which the hidden qualities of many familiar foods are revealed.

Many people think that valium is a 20th century invention. Incorrect! Apparently, humans and animals have been ingesting the drug for a long time. Scientists came across this eerie and astonishing fact when they detected the tranquilizer in the brains of wild and domesticated animals, deer, cows and chicken, as well as in eggs and cow's milk. None of the aforementioned have ever been prescribed the wonder drug. How then did it get there? The explanation is that the chemicals must be present in plants eaten for food; trace amounts were then "trapped" in the brain. Which foods? Scientists found them in potatoes, brown lentils, rice, corn, mushrooms and cherries, albeit in tiny amounts. No one has yet discovered the biological reason for these foods containing tranquilizers, but there is reason to believe that food-borne tranquilizers might serve as brain messengers or neuro transmitters. This is a tiny example of the wealth that lies in food.

Think of the common carrot. Its chief benefit — to decorate the top of a portion of gefilte fish? Good only for donkeys? Think again. A carrot is a super food source of beta carotene, which is a powerful anticancer, artery-protecting, immune-boosting, infection-fighting antioxidant, with wide protective powers. A carrot a day slashed stroke rates in women by 68 percent. One medium carrot's worth of beta carotene cuts lung cancer risk in half, even among former heavy smokers. High doses of beta carotene, as found in carrots, substantially reduce odds of degenerative eye diseases, as well as chest pains (angina). Carrots, which are high in soluble fiber, depress blood cholesterol, and promote regularity. It is worthwhile noting that cooking does not destroy the wonderful qualities of carrots; on the contrary, light cooking can make it easier for the body to absorb them. After hearing all that, you would be a donkey not to eat them.

Aspirin is one of the great "blood thinning," or anticoagulant drugs, and came originally from the bark of a willow tree. It was not until the 1970s that scientists began to understand just how aspirin works. They now know that the drug has anti-platelet-aggregation powers. That means that it discourages platelets, our smallest blood components, from clumping together, or aggregating. Thus, they are less sticky and less able to build clots that could clog arteries. Aspirin works by blocking action of a substance called thromboxane, which otherwise would stimulate platelets to stick together. Only one tenth of an aspirin — a mere 30 milligrams — inhibits platelet clumping. With this discovery, it was not a big leap to suggest that other plants and foods could also work to dampen blood platelets' enthusiasm to congregate. Like aspirin, some food compounds are antagonists to thromboxane; others, such as garlic and onions, contain several anti-platelet-clumping compounds that work in different biochemical ways. Cinnamon, cumin, fish oil, garlic, ginger, grapes, melon (both green and yellow), onion, tea, watermelon and red wine are all foods with anticoagulant powers. Marvelous!

You may recall that, according to rumor, our first major antibiotic, penicillin, was derived from moldy bread. Commercial penicillin used today is derived from a strain picked up on a moldy cantaloupe melon. With the commercial success of penicillin in the 1940s, scientists scrambled to find other natural bacteria destroyers to convert into drugs. One of the most promising candidates was garlic. Indeed, in 1858 Louis Pasteur noted that bacteria died when exposed to garlic. Garlic is one of the world's strongest, most complex, broad spectrum antibacterial agents. Tests have shown that garlic kills or cripples at least 72 infectious bacteria that spread diarrhea, dysentry and botulism, among other diseases. Onion, too, is an exceptionally strong antibiotic and antiseptic, and was used to treat infections in wounded Russian troops in World War II. Honey and wine were used on ancient Greek and Roman battlefields to clean and heal wounds. Food compounds destroy bacteria by several mechanisms, mainly by disrupting the bacteria's synthesis of protein and folic acid so they cannot multiply. Blueberries and cranberries not only inhibit bacteria, but also block their attachment to human cells. Here is a sample shopping list of delicious foods, all of which possess antibacterial properties: apple, banana, beet, cabbage, carrot, celery, chili pepper, coconut, garlic, honey, olive, plum, onion, wine and yogurt.

There are treasures for sale at your fruit store! How much does an orange cost? For just a few pennies you can acquire the orange, which is a complete package of goodness that inhibits the most serious illnesses known to man. Apart from that, the orange, because of its high vitamin C, may help ward off asthma and gum disease, as well as being beneficial to mankind in many notable ways.

Has anyone told you that greens are good for your mood? Or that you may be depressed because you are not eating enough fava beans or spinach? (If you can't stand spinach, this news will certainly depress you!) It sounds unlikely, but medical literature is astonishing in its agreement that folic acid deficiency — which is widespread in the United States — fosters psychiatric disorders, notably depression, but also dementia and schizophrenia. Folic acid is a B vitamin first isolated from green leafy vegetables. People deliberately deprived of folic acid in tests lapsed into sleeplessness, forgetfulness and irritability; restoring the vitamin caused the symptoms to disappear within two days. Green leafy vegetables (minus the insects) can do you a world of good.

The food pharmacy is as viable as the pill pharmacy, and more complex. No one has yet invented a "broccoli pill" that can match eating the real thing. A single food contains hundreds or thousands of chemicals, many unidentified, that can do tremendous good. It is no accident. When Hashem *Yisbarach* saw the world that He created — including the vast variety of natural foods — He declared it "very good." It is a statement that we would be wise to heed.

O ne of the interesting features of human nature is the ease with which the unusual can quickly become part of the accepted. Take the case of the plastic bag. Plastic is a relatively modern invention, but it has become an accepted part of society. One of its chief uses is in the manufacture of plastic bags. Once upon a time shoppers owned a fabric shopping bag, which accompanied them on every shopping trip — now, it is a rarity, since every store supplies a plastic bag to carry every single purchase, from a box of matches to a tub of ice cream. Most homes have plastic bags by the dozen, and usually possess large plastic bags to hold their smaller plastic bags. The ubiquitous plastic bag has numerous applications — including being worn over men's hats when it rains. Try and remember the very first time that you saw a man running through the rain wearing a plastic bag over his hat — what was your reaction? There is definitely something unusual at the sight of a grown man with a garbage bag perched on top of his head! Occasionally, the plastic bag actually fits the hat, but more commonly any old bag that comes to hand is used. At first, it must have caused a riot, but gradually, as more people adopted the custom, it became an accepted practice. Now, at the first drop of rain, you can wear any color, shape or size of plastic bag over your hat and no one will bat an eyelash. Such is human nature.

This helps to explain why it is that one of the most fascinating features of the created world passes most of us by without us paying it too much attention. If you left grass uncut, and allowed it to grow without interference, what height would it reach? If you have a wild, uncultivated garden, go out and look! It is rarely more than three feet. If the same question were asked about trees, what would your answer be? The sky is the limit. Before looking at the statistics, the question that needs answering is why grass does not grow as high as trees, or conversely, why are trees not as short as grass? Trees are so much part of our landscape (every kindergartener or first-grader's first picture is of a house with a tree standing — sometimes the correct way up — next to it) that we rarely notice them. They are there, because they are there. Who needs trees, what use have we from them, what would the world look like without them?

Try and imagine a world without wood, especially in the preplastic era. Since the first boat with an iron hull was built in Yorkshire, England, in the year 1777 (one year after the American Declaration of Independence), any sea travel before that time would have been impossible. Since all pre-1777 boats were constructed entirely from wood, all the distant continents, including North America and South America and Australia,

The mighty tree. Why doesn't grass grow that high?

would have waited centuries to be discovered In a world without wood, house construction would have been limited to brick, hides, or mud. Since bricks were once (and still are) an expensive commodity, out of the reach of most people's sparse income, people would effectively have been consigned to live their lives forever in mud huts. Without wood, there could have been no inland transport. People traveled by horse and cart. Horses come from horses — but where do carts come from? Without wood, man would have been isolated and homeless, unable to till the land or cross a river, or travel beyond the sea. Life would have remained harsh and isolated, poor and primitive.

Even now, living in a world of unimagined technical advancement, where the first word the little toddler utters has changed from "Da-da-da" to "Computa-ta-ta," where habitations of concrete, glass and plastic are the norm, take a look around your house and see just how many things are made of wood. The list is endless: the ceiling joists above your head; the floorboards beneath your feet; doors and window frames; the table in your dining room, with the chairs that surround it; the closet that stores your clothes; together with the breakfront that holds your candlesticks; the bookshelves; the banister and the stairs themselves. How could any cook worth her (or his) salt make a *cholent,* or anything for that matter, without a wooden spoon with which to stir it? Are you enjoying this article? Then thank the tree. Newsprint is chemically treated low-grade wood pulp. Once upon a time people used fabric handkerchiefs for their noses. No longer — it has to be a tissue. Kind-hearted people even buy boxes of them and donate them to *shuls* so that handkerchiefless *mispallelim* can find an immediate solution to any nasal crisis. It is flat, loosely woven fibers that give tissues their soft texture. The paper is made from wood pulp treated with plant resins to make it absorbent. From the *atzei chaim* to picture frames, from *mezuzah* cases to door handles, there is not an aspect of life that is not affected by wood.

A tree is a magnificent creation. The redwoods of California, which reach heights of 320 feet, are the tallest trees in the world. Some are so big, so nobly impressive, that they have been given their own individual names. One is the General Sherman. It stands 290 feet tall. Its girth, measured at six feet above the ground, is nearly 80 feet. Its trunk, branches, foliage and roots are estimated to weigh over 6000 tons. And this stupendous unparalleled accumulation of organic tissue has all been produced from a single seed weighing a fraction of an ounce. But before you get too carried away, just imagine what would happen if every blade of grass grew to such a gargantuan size — not only would you never be able to play golf, but you would actually be prevented from any mode of land travel due to the impenetrably thick forests that would grow everywhere. If every piece of vegetation grew to the size of even a modest pine tree (197 feet), no one would be able to build a house, for the spreading roots of enormous vegetation would undermine every single structure in the world. Man would walk like a Lilliputian, dwarfed by the gigantic structures that would enclose him in an endless, darkened forest.

What we in fact witness is a balance of inspiring proportions. Throughout the world there are scattered vast areas of grassland, which cover about one quarter of the land surface of the world. These are large, open areas of land covered in grass, where low bushes and a few trees may also grow. There cattle graze and crops are grown. Then there are forests. The world is blessed with coniferous forests (so called because their seeds are produced in cones). Vast coniferous forests of spruce, cedar, larch, pine and fir are found where conditions are cold and harsh. Deciduous forests of oak, beech, maple and ash, which require more temperate climates, are composed of trees that shed their leaves once a year. Then there are the much-discussed rainforests, which are found in a belt around the equator, where both the temperature and the amount of rainfall are high all year round. Inside a rain forest it is always hot, dark and damp. Enormous trees tower above the forest floor, forming a sort of roof which blocks out most of the sunshine. The canopy is so thick that rain can take 10 minutes to reach the ground! Rainforest trees never lose all their leaves at once. They are always green. Amazingly, the leaves of different trees never touch! This perfect balance, which is not accidental, means that there is space for everyone, and that precious wood-giving trees do not impose on human beings' ability to live in peace.

Do you ever buy flowers for Shabbos? Do you buy flowers each week? Would it not be more economical to buy them once a year? As everyone knows, even the most beautiful bouquet of blooms enjoys a very limited period of glory. Even after one week, they begin to wilt and the pristine beauty of the colorful flowers begins to fade. This was not arranged by the florists in order to increase business, but the result of the cellular makeup of the plant. Trees are different. If you happen to find yourself in the White Mountains of eastern California, especially at the height of 10,000 feet, you might come across some bristlecone pines. They will look stunted and ravaged, and the tallest of them will only be some 30 feet high. But do treat them with respect. They were already ancient when Columbus landed in the New World — in fact some of them are about 4,000 years old, the oldest trees in the world. How do they remain vibrant for so long? Why is it that if you fell wood, and cut it into timber, barring any invasion from outside infestation, the wood will remain firm and solid, seemingly forever? Think what would happen if wood had the same life expectancy as daffodils!

Wood does not rot or rust. It is available in all parts of the world, and in great abundance. It comes in different colors and varied textures. You can have softwood (for use in buildings) or hardwood (perfect for furniture). Wood is strong, yet easily carved or cut to any shape you wish. Compared to metal, it is light in weight, and floats on water. Compared to any other material, it is inexpensive. And most important of all — it is self-reproducing. When trees were created, an abundance of blessings came to the world. Those blessings of Creation are with us still, waiting to be appreciated, if we but open our eyes to see.

Special Protection

If you have ever visited London, the chances are that you went to — or wanted to go to — view the crown jewels. If so, you will not have been alone. Up to 15,000 people line up each day for the privilege of catching a fleeting glimpse at something of great value. There are two questions that everyone asks. Are the crown jewels real, and how much are they worth? The first question is easy to answer — yes, they are real, and if you visit the Jewel House on the day of the State Opening of Parliament, you will find the case housing the Imperial State Crown empty, because the crown will be in use. As to their value, it is not possible to estimate. The scepter itself is set with 393 gems, including the First Star of Africa, the world's largest cut diamond. The Imperial State Crown is set with 2,868 separate diamonds, 17 sapphires, 11 emeralds, 5 rubies and 273 pearls — real ones. How can anyone place a value on such wealth? If you would want to actually touch the jewels, for whatever reason. you would find it impossible. The security is virtually impenetrable. Shatterproof glass, alarms, guards, and closed-circuit surveillance are all utilized in guaranteeing the safety of the most valuable items in Britain.

It was not always so. In the latter part of the 1600s, when the present regalia was introduced, the crown jewels were kept, as now, in the Tower of London, on the ground floor. The residence above the jewels was occupied, not by the Master of the Jewel House (who had no desire to live in such miserable accommodations), but by a deputy. The deputy did not receive a salary, because no one could afford to pay him one. Instead, he was authorized to display the regalia to visitors for a small fee. He would do this by removing the crowns from a locked cupboard to show them! The inevitable was bound to happen. In April 1671, Colonel Thomas Blood, taking advantage of the lax and informal arrangements, attempted to steal the crown jewels. His daring plan was foiled only by the unexpected arrival of the deputy's son, and the robbers were apprehended and taken into custody. Since that time, security has been tightened constantly, culminating in today's situation where you cannot even take a photo of the invaluable and magnificent collection.

It makes sense that anything of value should be well protected. If the principle holds true with jewels, how much more so with the vital organs on which our lives depend. If you are reading this, there is a very good chance that you are using your brain. It is almost axiomatic that there is no organ more central, more vital to the physical well-being of a person than his brain. No computer exists that can duplicate all its myriad functions. The brain has a huge number of jobs. It controls

The queen of England's crown. Would you like to be responsible for its protection?

the circulatory, digestive, and respiratory systems. It monitors the concentrations of substances such as glucose and carbon dioxide in blood, adjusts fluids and nutrient levels, and dozens of other body processes that occur every minute. The brain screens the gigantic amounts of information that are continuously gathered by the senses, and filters out all but the most important features. (You have a power to concentrate on what you wish to see, hear, and even think. If you tell yourself not to think of a certain subject, you will not think of it.) Our knowledge of the brain is less complete than our knowledge of most other organs. This is due to the astonishingly complicated microstructure of this wonder organ, which is comprised of 30 billion neurons, and up to 10 times that number of cells. Each cell is as complicated as a city. All that is in a space that fits into your size 7 hat! Nothing is more complex, nothing more precious. How is it protected?

The brain resides in a well-protected fortress. This fortress is the *cranium,* commonly known as the skull. The skull is a quarter of an inch thick at the top, and even thicker at the base. Do not think of the cranium as a single seamless case — it in fact consists of 22 separate bones. These bones fit together like linking pieces of a jigsaw. Interestingly, when a baby is born it has fingernails and eyelashes. But the bones of its skull do not join together for some months after birth. This is not an oversight, but rather an ingeniously designed system to allow the bones of the cranium to overlap during the birth process, thereby expediting a successful entry into the world. Care has to be taken in the baby's early months not to press on the soft areas of the skull (*the fontanels*).

There is another good reason why the skull is comprised of a network of bones as opposed to a single bone. If a person suffered — Heaven forbid — a severe bump on the head, there would be some internal bleeding, which we would recognize as a bruise. If all the bones were one, the bruise with its attendant internal bleeding would spread over the whole cranial area, greatly aggravating the situation. By separating the bone into sections, the injury remains localized and a speedier recovery is facilitated.

An additional advantage in the cranium comprising several bones is that it allows different parts of the skull to be of varied thicknesses. The *temporal bones* (the two bones at the sides, above and around the ears) are the hardest bones in the body. They have to be, to give added protection to the delicate hearing mechanism that resides within. The tough bone surrounding the ear also acts as a resonator to the vibrations of sound reaching the ear, much like the wooden casing of the guitar enhances the sound of the plucked strings. The bones of the forehead and the lower face, in contrast, are much thinner, accommodating the vast variety of facial features that give each person their unique and individual appearance.

Inside the cranium, the brain is surrounded by several protective membranes and fluids. These membranes are called *meninges,* and their function is to give added protection to the wonder computer that lies within. Within the spaces formed by the various layers runs a marvelous fluid called *cerebrospinal fluid* (CSF). This fluid is separate and different from the normal blood supply, and it has its own production factory. It is formed from two masses of fine blood capillaries in the roof of the brain. This fluid, which extends down the spinal column, is kept circulating by tiny cilia (microscopic hairs) which extend into the fluid and vibrate gently. Special valves between the layers of membrane surrounding the brain prevent the rest of our blood from entering the CSF.

It is obvious to everyone with a brain in their cranium that moving paddles (cilia) and valves are functional objects that have a specific job which is vital to the whole operation of which they are part. You cannot have half a valve or a quarter of a paddle. They are mechanisms that must work perfectly to work at all, and that each in turn is as functional as — a paddle and a valve. No valve in the world makes itself, and no boat's paddle has ever appeared by accident.

The CSF serves as a shock absorber, so the brain is cushioned from damage when the person jumps around or bangs his head. At the same time, it will be clear that constant banging can hardly be advantageous, which is the reason why the "sport" of boxing is one of the most dangerous and foolhardy. Imagine taking a sledgehammer and thumping your computer for a solid hour! Don't try it. The CSF has another vital function. It acts as a barrier, a gatekeeper that allows some things in, while denying entry to others. Thus, it welcomes glucose, but blocks out bacteria and toxic substances. Most painkillers and anesthetics pass in with ease, but so, unfortunately, does alcohol and hallucinogenic drugs that wildly distort reality.

The brain is not the only vital organ in the body. The heart and lungs are as precious to the individual as the crown jewels are to Great Britain. How many bumps and thumps does a person endure? Imagine that the lungs and heart were without protection — how would one endure the pain and injury? The rib cage that protects these organs is just what it is called — a cage. By means of this enclosure, the vital organs are protected from mishap. Imagine yourself ice-skating for the first time. As you wobble away from the safety of the wall, life suddenly loses its stability. The likelihood is that within a very short time, you will make full body contact with the cold unyielding ice. The bigger the skater, the harder the fall. The rib cage is there to protect its precious contents. Even if a rib is broken, it will mend itself. No other cage does that. Apart from its protective role, the rib cage is a flexible unit, whose constant movements up and down are vital ingredients in the breathing process. The rib cage also supports your arms. In the human body, nothing, absolutely nothing, is simple. Everything is complex, clever, and interconnected.

The protection surrounding the crown jewels serves a vital purpose. An outside intelligence, recognizing their value, has designed and constructed the appropriate security system. It neither happened by accident, nor did the jewels, realizing their special role in English heritage, commission their friends the lumps of iron to come to their assistance. The One Who designed the complex brain, vital lungs and living heart also commissioned their protection. Look closely at the head, and you will see its Creator.

The Staff of Life

ou will be forgiven for not having heard of Otto Frederick Rohwedder. But you will certainly have heard of his invention. When his innovation was perfected in 1928, it was not, surprisingly, hailed as "the greatest thing since sliced bread," for reasons that will soon become clear. His invention was in fact the bread-slicing machine. He began work on his machine in 1915, in the face of fierce opposition from the bakery trade who asserted that sliced bread would dry out too fast. In order to hold the slices together, he designed a machine to impale them on sterile hatpins, but the pins invariably fell out. His next idea was to pack the slices in shallow boxes lined with grease-proof paper. That too proved impractical. Eventually he hit on the solution that was to make sliced bread a success: a machine which cut the bread and then sealed it in a wrapper. By the year 1933, 80 percent of all the bread sold in America was precut, and by the end of the decade, people were already saying, about anything that gladdened their hearts, that it was "the greatest thing since sliced bread."

Well done, Otto! His invention certainly made life easier for people who prefer their bread toasted, and for those whose cutting skills are erratic. Interestingly enough, the prediction made in a Britain newspaper in 1930 that "before long, bread would be sold already buttered" was never fulfilled. Anyone who seeks to fill that inventor's niche will justifiably be able to claim to have provided humanity with the greatest thing since ... !

To invent a slicing machine is one thing. To invent the substance which is sliced in the machine is another matter entirely. Think of it this way. There are many hundreds of millions of people in the world. They all have stomachs and all need feeding — not just once in a while, but generally at least twice each day. What food could you produce which could satisfy the following requirements: It must provide carbohydrates, proteins and fats in sufficient quantities to sustain the consumer, and keep him healthy and strong. It must be ready available throughout the world, in varying climates and lands. It must be cheap to produce, and inexpensive to purchase. It must be sufficiently versatile to be processed in a variety of shapes and sizes, flavors and styles to cater to the widest possible variety of tastes. If all you had was barren earth, would you be able to produce bread?

There is no food in the world more widely eaten than bread. It provides a larger share of people's energy and proteins than any other food, and is rightly called "the staff of life." You can eat what you like for breakfast. Begin with fruit juice, have a coffee and two soft-boiled eggs, dig into a grapefruit, lavish

No food in the world is more widely eaten than bread.

yourself with cake or cookies; be an Englishman and devour a couple of kippers; be a health fanatic and sip your way through a yogurt — even have some cereal ("start your day with the sunshine breakfast") — nothing will satisfy you like bread. None of the bread substitutes are as good as the real thing. You can be health conscious, trying to slim down, pushed for time, a vitamin fanatic — if you do not eat bread, you will not be satisfied. Halfway through the morning, your stomach will develop a vacuum, and the nagging emptiness of hunger will spread inexorably across your midriff. The Gemara in *Bava Metzia* 107b lists no less than 13 benefits in eating bread — not least of them the peace of mind that feeling satisfied produces. According to the Gemara, no one should attempt to teach without having had bread for his breakfast. A hungry teacher is an irritable teacher, and an irritable teacher is not a good teacher. If you want to teach well, prepare your lessons, and butter your bread for breakfast.

Bread is made by baking dough. Dough in turn consists chiefly of flour or grain meal mixed with water or milk. The people of Western countries eat bread baked mainly as loaves or rolls made with wheat flour. In some other parts of the world, people eat thin, crisp sheets of bread called flatbread. (Ever heard of matzah?) Flatbread is made either from such grains as barley, corn, oats, rice, rye, and wheat, or from flour milled from these grains.

Wheat, the chief ingredient of bread, is a marvelous food. High-fiber whole wheat and particularly wheat bran rank as the world's greatest preventives of constipation. Food works as a natural laxative in several complex ways. High fiber foods, such as bran, contain coarse particles that mechanically activate nerve reflexes in the lower-intestine wall, triggering elimination. According to authoritative medical opinion, constipation often results from a deficiency in high-fiber foods. Earlier generations ate about 1¼ pounds of whole grain, high-fiber bread a day. We eat only one fifth as much, a mere 4 ounces, and most of it made from highly refined white flour that is fiber depleted. Bran is potent in preventing serious illnesses. Remarkably, wheat bran can suppress polyps (small growths) that could develop into more serious ailments. Barley has long been known as a "heart medicine" in the Middle East. It is known to reduce cholesterol. This is similar to oats, which also has an anti-cholesterol capacity. Apart from which, oats help to stabilize blood sugar. In addition, oats contain psychoactive compounds that may combat nicotine cravings and have antidepressant powers. What modern science is discovering today was known by our *chachamim* at least 1500 years ago when they compiled the Gemara.

Wheat is grown extensively throughout the world.

Interestingly enough, breeders have reduced the amount of stalk, so that the plant does not bend over and make it difficult to harvest the grain. This assists the major grain-producing countries in the world (of which China is the biggest) where vast quantities of wheat are grown. Bread wheat, which is the most widely grown species of wheat, has large grains which have a high gluten content. Gluten makes bread dough elastic, and enables light fluffy bread to be made. Durum wheat (or macaroni wheat, as it is sometimes known), in contrast, is grown widely today to provide the flour for pasta and biscuits. Because its gluten content is minimal, it does not make good bread, but is marvelous for macaroni, spaghetti, semolina, not to mention *heimishe farfel* and couscous.

What makes bread particularly appealing is its pleasant aroma, and its airy light texture. Without the holes, the bread would be flat, hard and unappealing. Where do the holes come from? They in fact emanate from bubbles of gas. A dough is formed by mixing flour and water. Then, a small amount of yeast (*se'or*) is added to the mixture. Yeast is a type of fungus which grows very quickly when it is warm and damp, and acts as a leavening agent. While growing, it releases a gas which bubbles up through the dough, making it expand. It is yeast which gives bread its particular flavor and appetizing smell. (Cakes also have holes in them made by bubbles of gas. But these are made by a different substance which leaves practically no flavor. This substance is baking powder, which is a mixture of tartaric acid and bicarbonate of soda. When these two chemicals are mixed together, moistened and heated, they react to produce carbon dioxide. This gas bubbles through the cake mixture to make it rise while it is being baked.)

It is an interesting phenomenon that things that are the least thought of are usually the most important. (In similar vein, it is said that if the president and the garbage collectors went on strike simultaneously, people would miss the services of the garbagemen long before they noticed the absence of the president.) Wheat is a type of grass, and yeast is a fungus. Grass is so common and widespread that apart from its color, it is rarely noticed or remarked about. No one stands up to honor fungus. Quite the contrary, should you notice fungus in your home, you are less than happy. Yet, without these two humble commodities, the staple diet of the majority of the world would simply not exist. Hunger would stalk the world.

The fact that wheat, and its subsidiaries can be grown virtually anywhere in the world, is not accidental. If, like pineapples, it could only be grown in equatorial regions, it would be of little use to the masses of the world's population. It is an interesting fact that of the four species at Succos-time, three of them (*lulav*, *esrog*, and *hadassim*) grow only in the hot Mediterranean region. And they are all long lasting. If they would have had a short shelf life, how could they have been distributed throughout the Jewish world in the days before air freight? The fourth species, *aravos*, dries up within days. Not surprisingly, the willow can be found all over the world, in temperate as well as hot climates. There was never a need to export *aravos*. The One Who gave the *mitzvos* created the trees! In exactly the same way, the Creator of mankind ensured that there would always be food available to feed him, and feed him well, wherever he lives.

"Hazan es ha'olam kulo b'tuvo b'chen b'chesed uv'rachamim ..."

The Long Sleep

Rip Van Winkle was an amiable but lazy farmer who lived in a village at the foot of the Catskills in the good old days when America was still a British colony. One day, while walking with his dog and gun in the mountains, he met an old man dressed in quaint costume. The elderly gentleman asked his help in carrying a barrel of liquor. Rip accompanied him, and met a group of similarly attired strange old men. They gave him large quantities of gin to drink, whereupon he fell into a deep sleep. Waking, as he thinks, the next morning, he found his dog gone, and his gun barrel rusted. He was stiff in the joints, his clothes were ragged and, most interesting of all, he had a long grey beard. He descended to his village and found it completely changed, and that no one recognized him. He was a stranger in his own village! He had in fact been asleep for 20 years, and the hosts who gave him the gin were the ghostly crew of the explorer Henry Hudson. Rip Van Winkle gradually gets his bearings, and finds himself a role as the oldest inhabitant of the village, forever telling stories of his strange experience, and what life was like before the big sleep.

This story, popularized by Washington Irving, was claimed to be based on a traditional German tale. It is likely that both the American and the European versions of the tale were based on the true story of Choni *Hama'agel*, related in *Taanis* 23a. In that event, Choni slept for 70 years. When he awoke, he was so upset that not a single person recognized him that he asked to be taken from the world.

The ability to sleep for such extended periods is a rare, even miraculous occurrence in humans. Animals, on the other hand, manage it extremely well, and with great regularity. Every year, as the temperature drops, different animals cope with the onset of winter in a variety of fascinating ways. One of them is by hibernation, in which the animal quite simply goes to sleep for months at a time. At the first sign of winter, Asian and American black bears find themselves a cave, a hole in a tree, or just a good deep pile of leaves and drift off to sleep until spring.

How do they survive without food for so long? Food is scarce during winter, so the bears eat as much as they can in the summer and autumn and convert the excess calories into body fat. A lean bear in late autumn is usually dangerous; feeling that he has not supplied an urgent need, he becomes irritable and often savage. In addition, they conserve energy by their big sleep. (Energy burns calories. The less energetic you are, the less you need to eat, and the less hungry you are. That is why during an extended *Yom Tov* period, with longer hours of *davening*, and extra hours of sleeping, you actually feel less inclined to eat than during a normal weekday.) In slumber, the bears' body temperature may drop by as much as 9 degrees Fahrenheit and their metabolic rate by 50 percent.

The polar bear mother does not eat a thing from November until about March. During this time, holed up in the Arctic snow, she gives birth to up to four cubs and nurses them. Her youngsters are utterly dependent on her rich milk for the first three months of their lives. To supply this life-giving milk, and to nourish herself, the mother bear subsists on the thick layer of fat beneath her skin, built up in the summer months when food was plentiful. Even when the bear family has emerged from the den and the cubs start taking solid food, their mother has to share all her catches of fish and seals with them. So by spring, she is only half the weight she was six months earlier, at the end of the previous summer. Think a little. Who is it that taught the bears to eat voraciously to prepare for the long sleep? Who arranged that excess food should be converted to fat (stored energy) rather than be eliminated through the digestive process? Who is it who trained them to lower their body metabolism and their temperature (remember that bears, like humans, are warm-blooded animals whose body temperature is automatically regulated to remain at a constant)? Who educated them to go to sleep for months on end? Who provided the mechanisms of these vital systems and the instincts that trigger them? It all points to a mighty Intelligence.

Up north in Canada, where the winters are long and severe, the painted turtles live. These turtles hatch from their leathery eggs in autumn. Once hatched, you would expect them to begin their active life immediately. That is what most people do, but not the painted turtle. Before emerging into the world, they will spend their first winter in the nest. Almost immediately after birth they have to survive the cold — they do so by hibernating. Female painted turtles nest in midsummer in south-facing banks. (Having learned geography, they know which way is south.) Then, in the frigid cold, these turtles survive the winter in the same way as so many mammals, by hibernating. During the long winter months, the tiny turtles go into a torpor, eating nothing and barely moving. Their bodies contain a natural antifreeze that enables them to survive for long periods when the temperature in the nest drops below freezing. Now isn't that something? Here is a revolutionary method of saving money. Remove the central heating from your home, and this winter, program your body to produce antifreeze in the blood Supply. However cold the weather, you'll never feel cold. Go ahead — arrange it!

Many people wonder where all the flies go in the winter. Shortly after Succos, they all seem to disappear, and not a one is to be seen throughout the long winter months. Six months later, after Pesach, out they come again. Are they the same ones, and if so, where do they hide? The answer is that during winter, flies will hibernate, sometimes in large groups, in any available dry and warm space such as an attic. They are fast asleep and out of sight. The reason there are so few houseflies in winter is that their eggs will hatch only at temperatures between 75 and 90 degrees Fahrenheit. Meanwhile, their numbers steadily diminish owing to insecticides and natural causes. Since flies are often carriers of diseases, it is not a bad thing that their numbers diminish during the long sleep. Bees, on the other hand, do not hibernate; they have their honey to live on, and they keep up their own temperature by closely clustering, constantly vibrating their wings to elevate the hive temperature.

During the period of suspended existence, not only does the hibernator's temperature drop to almost half of normal, but the heart slows down, and all functions of alimentation and excretion cease. Respiration is faint, and in some sleeps appears to wholly cease. Don't try this, but a hibernating bat was once submerged in a bucket of water for an hour; when taken out, it was still asleep and perfectly healthy despite its ordeal.

It is not only by hibernating that animals are able to survive the winter. Listen to this amazing fact. Everyone knows that when the temperature drops, fingers, toes and ears freeze first. But it has been only within the last 200 years that we have understood that this is due to the ratio between the amount of body surface through which heat can be lost, and the body's bulk and heat supply. (This explains why mittens are warmer than gloves; the fingers of a glove have more radiating surface than the mass of a mitten.) About 100 years ago, physicists working on the kinetic theory of gases found that heat travels very slowly through still air. Applying this knowledge of dead-air space to our cold-weather clothes, manufacturers have developed coats and jackets with light, airy padding. Progress!

Now although you and I have been in possession of the above-mentioned information for a relatively short time, deer have been using these principles since they were created. With the first autumnal frosts, the deer shed their cool summer coat and grow a special one for winter. Each hair of this winter coat is hollow, like a small tube sealed at the outer end. This effectively covers the deer with a layer of still air, trapped within the hairs. Covered with this air blanket, deer can walk the winter wilderness almost without the need for shelter. You knew nothing, and the deer knew much less than you, yet somehow he knew that he ought to be growing a hollow-haired coat for winter. Where exactly did the deer obtain its knowledge of the laws of advanced kinetic energy? Was it Deer College, or perhaps Reindeer University? A Great Intelligence is clearly indicated.

In autumn the squirrel builds a loose ball of a nest, using dry leaves and twigs. Curled inside this airy mass when the snow flies, he becomes his own furnace, heating the still air around him until he is locked in comfort. In the depth of winter, a woodpecker lies in the cozy hollow of a tree. Inside, surrounded by wood and out of the wind, he fluffs his feathers — the most amazing insulating material in existence. Wrapped in motionless air, he needs to heat only himself. Outside, the temperature can be below zero. Inside his very own quilt, he will be a warm 104 degrees.

Ail the wisdom inherent in the animals, their ability to survive a six-month sleep, to keep warm without clothes, antifreeze and insulation, did not come to them by chance. Nor did it come from themselves. Wisdom and intelligence always emanate from a Higher Intelligence.

Mibsari echezeh Elokai.

The Pony Express

You might have heard of a gentleman by the name of Buffalo Bill. Besides his expertise with a six-gun, and his unpopularity amongst the American Indian fraternity, he was in fact a postman. During the year 1860, William Cody (alias "Buffalo Bill") delivered letters between two cities in America; St. Joseph in Missouri and Sacramento in California for the famous Pony Express. The route covered 1,838 miles and included 157 stations, which lay from seven to 20 miles apart. The expert riders were chosen to ride fast horses which were changed six to eight times on the scheduled ride. The time schedule for the run was 10 days, but this was only occasionally achieved.

The Pony Express might not have been the fastest service in the world (it was actually discontinued in October 1861 when the completion of the transcontinental telegraph ended its usefulness), but it was certainly more reliable than the earlier method of sending messages, which was by carrier pigeon. People who used this method of communication had to send a duplicate letter by a different pigeon in case the first bird met a hawk on the way! Sending out wedding invitations must have presented a nightmare. Prospective guests either received two invitations or none, and if the pigeon could not read your writing (or ran out of birdseed halfway through the journey) you really were in a pickle.

Things have improved somewhat since those hazardous days. Today, the postal services of the world combine to make a planet-sized brain of stupendous complexity. Most of the world's 6.5 billion people could communicate with almost anyone else by mail within a few days, if they wish. The quantity of mail handled by the world's 654,000 post offices is staggering. On any one day, almost one billion items pass through the international postal system. Apart from complications like weekends and holidays, ungainly parcels and illegible envelopes, strikes and breakdowns, and other factors that often combine to force delays, every delivery is a minor tribute to human ingenuity and cooperation.

But even the best that human ingenuity can provide, whether through pigeons, ponies or postmen, pales into insignificance when compared to the distribution system of your own body in the manner in which food is placed into the mouth and then distributed to a trillion addresses. The fascinating thing is that the distribution system of the mail begins when the sender puts a letter into the mailbox. What happens if the sender does not feel like writing his letter and mailing it? How will the would-be recipient inform his friend that he is longing for some communication? Using this analogy in the created world, how does the body inform itself that

One of the thousand million items posted each day

some food is required? There is an answer — and it might be calling you right now — it's called hunger.

It is a remarkable thing. When you drive a car, or any motor-driven vehicle, the fuel gauge informs the driver how much fuel there is in the tank. As fuel is burned on a journey, the indicator approaches the zero marker. If the driver is trained to keep a careful watch on his fuel consumption, he will know that he has to refuel before he runs out of fuel. If he is careless, or new to the pleasures of driving, it is possible that he might ignore the fuel gauge, or be ignorant of its message. The sad plight of a car stranded in the middle of nowhere with an empty tank is not unknown! Such an occurrence could never happen with people or with animals. Hunger is the feeling that guarantees the survival of us all. If you come home late from *davening*, quickly swallow a gulp of coffee and a piece of cake for your breakfast before rushing out to learn, teach or work, the alarm bells will begin ringing in your stomach approximately halfway through the morning informing you in an unmistakable manner that you need to take on more fuel. Imagine if you never felt hungry. Busy people would skip their meals, rush around expending energy until they collapsed due to lack of food and drink. When children come home from school and race into the kitchen with an agonized cry, "I'm starving!", there is a clear indication that their fuel gauge is not only registering empty, but it is actually informing them of the fact in a most remarkable manner.

Like everything in the created world, hunger is anything but simple. A complex system of nerves in the digestive tract, together with chemical sensors, send urgent messages to the *hypothalumus* (the brain stem) which the brain interprets as hunger. Your stomach feels the hunger, but it is your brain that delivers the information. The message is unmistakable. Find food. It's time to mail the letter.

Ever seen a man on the prowl for food? He comes into the kitchen with a distracted look on his face. His wife might want to tell him of the latest antics of their infant, or of the exemplary *middos* of their teenager — he is not interested. Cupboards open and slam shut. The refrigerator is turned upside down. The husband becomes frantic. The cake is located ... contents ingested ... now you can talk.

When you put a letter into the mailbox, you are initiating a complex process that ultimately will bring the posted item safely to its destination. You do not have to be an expert in your knowledge of all the details; it is sufficient to rely on the efficiency of the postal system. When you swallow a morsel of food, the distribution system is even more complex, and ever a superficial understanding of its complexity will lead to an enhanced appreciation of the Creator of the magnificent system.

When the piece of food vanishes into the mouth, it is beginning a journey that is almost 30 feet long. Each section of the digestive system has its own definitive role. The gullet is a transfer tube linking the mouth to the stomach. The stomach is a food squasher and chemical bath. (In addition to enzymes, the stomach lining makes corrosive hydrochloric acid. This eats away at the food and helps to kill germs that have entered the body in the food. To stop itself from being digested by its own enzymes and acid, the stomach lining produces a thick layer of slimy mucus. As the stomach contents ooze along to the small intestine, they encounter pancreatic juices which contain an alkali. This counteracts the stomach acid, so that it does not harm the rest of the digestive tract.) The small intestine finishes food breakdown and carries out absorption. The large intestine, like the best recycling factory, re-absorbs valuable leftovers of the digestive process into the body, such as minerals from the digestive juices and water. The end of the large intestine stores leftovers, and awaits a convenient time to expel them.

The process is aided by the teeth that cut and chew the food; by the tongue that moves the food around for thorough chewing and mixing with saliva; by the liver that processes and stores nutrients, and produces bile salts; by the gall bladder that stores bile salts — used to break up fats and oils — and empties them into the intestine; and by the pancreas that makes pancreatic juices containing digestive enzymes.

Each section of the system is a wonder of design, and the more one investigates, the more one discovers. To an observer, the digestive system might seem one of the easier body systems to understand. In fact, it was not until the 19th century that the chemistry of the digestive process was understood in detail. The whole process of digestion is like dismantling a building brick by brick — including the doors, windows, floorboards, and roof tiles — and then putting these parts back together according to another set of plans, to make a completely different building. In this comparison, the first building is the food, while the second building is your body tissue.

Food contains not only energy, but also the raw materials needed for the body's growth, maintenance, and repair. It is as if you put gasoline into a car's tank, and then watched the car convert the gasoline into replacement bearings, nuts and bolts, and new tires for itself! To carry out its maintenance and repair processes, the body needs a selection of nutrients, such as proteins, carbohydrates, fats and oils, minerals and vitamins. The huge molecules of carbohydrates, proteins, and lipids are too big to pass through the lining of the intestines and become absorbed into the body. Digestion breaks these large food substances into their subunits, so that they are small enough to pass through. With digestion, proteins are split into amino acids, carbohydrates into sugars, and lipids into fatty acids. These subunits are carried around the body in both blood and lymph, and supplied to each and every cell. In each cell, the nutrients are used according to the cell's needs — perhaps to provide energy or to make new substances.

In the postal system, you pay a lot of money for a special service that guarantees delivery on the next day. To carry your package across continents, can take many days. In your body's superb operation, you mail your letter in the morning, and by lunchtime every particle of it has been distributed through the thousands of miles of the internal transport system to every one of the body's trillions of individual cells. No system could be more complex and as efficient. No system could be better planned. Think of the postal system and think of your stomach. There you see the greatness of the Creator.

Gold Rush – for Calcium

In the summer of 1896, an Indian fighter called Skookum Jim discovered gold in a stretch of water named Bonanza Creek. Until that momentous occasion, Bonanza Creek had been a nondescript tributary of the Klondike River in the Yukon Territory of NW Canada. Some gold had already been found in other parts of the Yukon area, but this find was richer than any of the earlier ones. Within eight days, Skookum Jim and two of his relatives took some 80 ounces of gold from the muddy waters of the stream. Miners working on other sites in the neighborhood hurried to the site, where they found other rich deposits of gold in a stream flowing into Bonanza Creek. The news spread southwards, and by midsummer 1897, a new town called Dawson City was housing 4,000 people in log cabins. A year later, Dawson's population mushroomed to 20,000 — adventurers, miners, fortune hunters and fraudsters — all searching for the illusive metal. A year later, however, the great rush came to an end, the population of Dawson began to dwindle, and by 1910 most of the people had left. Nowadays, Dawson City has but a few hundred inhabitants, and the search for gold has moved elsewhere.

Anyone who is really interested in locating precious substances does not have to travel as far as the Yukon, nor do they have to visit a jeweler. In fact, wherever you go, the precious material goes with you. It's in your bones. It's calcium. Who needs it?

Calcium is an essential nutrient which must be provided regularly in the diet. It is the most abundant mineral in the body, constituting about 2 percent of total body weight (average man's weight 168 pounds — 3.3 pounds of calcium), most of it to be found in the bones. An adequate intake of calcium is vital for the structural integrity of the bones and teeth.

Structural engineers have long acknowledged the combination of strength and lightness given by bones. Weight for weight, bone is stronger than wood, concrete, or steel. If the human skeleton were made of enough steel to equal the strength of bone, it would weigh five times as much. This remarkable strength comes mainly from its inner structure. It is built up from thousands of compactly arranged, tube-shaped units, each called a Haversian system. The units are named after the English physician Mr. Clopton Havers, who discovered the wonder of bones and calcium in 1691. He discovered that the bone tissue in the walls of these tubes is made of fibers of the protein *collagen*, which give it elasticity, and mineral crystals, including calcium, which make it hard. A Haversian system is only one hundredth of an inch in diameter. (It was only the discovery of the microscope in the 1600's that made this discovery possible.) It is made from

Care for a glass of calcium?

thousands of fibers of collagen embedded in mineral salts of calcium and phosphorus. The fibers are laid in circular layers (called *lamellae*) like the growth rings you see in a sliced-through tree trunk. How exactly does it work?

Imagine that you had made a tower of straws pointing in all directions. Then, you made a second tower with the same number of straws, placed upright in a tubular formation. If you placed a board on top of the two formations, and pressed down, the random arrangement would soon collapse, whereas the ring of straws design is much stronger. Imagine that you now placed the ring of straws inside a tube — in effect a tube of tubes — and pressed down with the board. It will be much stronger than the circle of loose tubes in the first experiment. This tube of tubes is a simple model of the shaft of a long bone. The straws are the Haversian systems, and the space in the middle is the bone-marrow cavity. It goes without saying, but needs saying nevertheless, that when a skyscraper is built, the engineers take careful consideration of the strength of the building materials. They also take into account the size, shape and arrangement of the main supporting parts, such as steel girders or concrete pillars. No building ever stands that was erected at random! If so, who is the designing Engineer of the tower of strength that constitutes the skeletal bones? Who invented and provided the vital building constituent, calcium?

You can get around without a bike, you can manage without a Borsalino, but there is no substitute for calcium, for a number of reasons. Bones develop in two ways. Many, including the long bones, appear early as the child develops even before birth. Those bones first appear as cartilage, which is gradually calcified in late pregnancy and after birth. Others, such as the flat bones of the skull, are formed without an intermediate cartilage-stage. Bones grow at different rates. Some, for example, those of the skull, grow slowly, but the long bones of the limbs are capable of rapid growth, especially during the years of adolescence. Even when growth in length stops in the late teens, slower growth continues as the shoulders and hips broaden. In fact, bones continue to thicken and increase in density and strength into the 30s and 40s, at which point peak bone mass (PBM) is said to have been reached. This whole process of growing involves a considerable accumulation of calcium, all of which must be provided by the diet.

Everyone knows that getting your calcium (otherwise known as drinking your milk) helps build strong bones. And keeping strong bones can help save you from *osteoporosis*, that progressive bone-thinning disease that haunts over 2 million people in Great Britain. One in three women and at least one in 20 men are affected by osteoporosis, resulting in 30 percent of orthopedic beds being taken by osteoporosis fracture-patients. The best-known mineral with clout to ward off osteoporosis is calcium. It both builds strong bones and helps keep them from weakening in later years. There is no doubt that it is best to load up on calcium to create strong bones while still young. Researchers at Indiana University recently studied groups of identical twins, ages 6-14. They found that the twin who received double the calcium until bar mitzvah-age had bones that were up to 5 percent denser than the twin who merely ate the daily recommended allowance. Researchers claim that this definitely gave the high calcium-consuming children the edge, and such children have about a 40 percent lower risk of fractures in later life.

A string of studies shows that eating calcium when you are young equals stronger bones and fewer fractures when older. But what are you to do if you suffered a deprived childhood, and grew up with lots of love and affection, but little calcium? Eating calcium will not build bones after the age of 30, that is, increase their mass. However, absorbing sufficient calcium after that age is still important, because it helps retard bone loss, preventing fractures. Although milk is rich in calcium, not everyone finds that milk agrees with them. Don't despair. All dairy foods are high in calcium. If milk is not to your (stomach's) liking, try yogurt or cheese. Canned mackerel with bones or canned salmon with bones is also high in calcium, as are dried figs (minus the insects), baked beans, and that favorite of *sholom zochers* — cooked chickpeas.

A word of warning might be in place. There are grounds to believe that the pasteurization of milk, important though it is, actually reduces its calcium content. This is born out by the greater incidence of calcium deficiency-related maladies, such as bone fractures and arthritis, compared to earlier times. While on the subject, it is important to know that too much salt can also rob bones of calcium, especially in the elderly. New Zealand researchers first put elderly women on a low-salt diet, then switched them to a high-salt diet. They ate the same quantities of calcium on both diets. Yet, on the high-salt diet, about 30 percent more calcium was flushed out of the body, diverting it away from the bones. This could be detrimental at any age, but especially to elderly women at high risk of bone fracture.

As important as calcium is for strong, healthy bones, it has other functions too, and no less vital for health. Calcium is present in blood and other body fluids. Although only 1 percent of the body's calcium is to be found in the blood, it is essential to the activity of many metabolic processes. In fact, human life is dependent on the proper balance between the supply of calcium and its processing within cells. The process of blood clotting requires calcium ions at a number of stages in the cascade of chemical stages that must occur in the correct sequence to enable blood to solidify at the site of a wound.

Calcium is recommended as a secret weapon against high blood pressure. Some experts are of the opinion that high blood pressure is more likely due to a deficiency of calcium than to a surplus of sodium (salt), and in fact, that adequate calcium can cancel the blood pressure-raising effects of sodium in some people.

Life might be less glittery, but you can live without gold. A humble mineral, called calcium, costs pennies in the drugstore, but we cannot exist without it. We need it, so it's there — in every glass of milk, in each dried fig, and in every piece of cheese. This world was created with precision and planning. Nothing is lacking in Hashem's world.

The Amazing Nut Case

You might not believe it, but it's true. There is a Frenchman by the name of Michel Lotito who eats about 2 pounds of metal a day. Since 1966, he has munched his way through several bicycles (including tires and metal filings), supermarket carts, and television sets (the metal and glass were no problem, but some of the programs must have made him sick) together with cutlery and razor blades. He has also eaten a whole light aircraft, which took him two years to finish. On average, it takes him about four days to chew his way through a supermarket cart. No one should be surprised.

Human beings are capable of eating the strangest of objects, especially if the object of their appetite is to gain fame and glory in the record books. For example, there is a gentleman in the United States who can swallow one complete liter of beer in two seconds. How would you like to eat 17 bananas in 2 minutes? A hungry doctor in California did so recently! Do you have a fancy for eggs? Would you care for 14 hard-boiled ones in 58 seconds; or might you prefer 32 soft-boiled ones in 78 seconds? Both feats have been performed in front of witnesses (who no doubt kept a respectful distance). You might think that these record-seekers are nuts — but they eat those too. Mr. James Kornitzer of Brighton, England, managed to down 100 whole unshelled peanuts in 46 seconds one summer's day.

Peanuts are one thing. Brazil nuts are quite another. Monsieur Lotito can munch through his light aircraft, but it is doubtful if he could make any headway on a Brazil nut. A young man recently brought some Brazil nuts for his family as a treat. Out came the trusty nutcracker to do battle. The nutcracker lost. After struggling with one hard nut, the central bolt that linked the two sides of the nutcracker flew out, and in the second round, one of the metal sides of the implement actually cracked.

The reason that Brazil nuts are so called is, not surprisingly, because they grow in Brazil. The nuts are produced inside a large round capsule by the bertholletia tree that grows in the Brazilian rain forest. When it lands with a thump on the forest floor, it nearly always remains intact. We have to appreciate the design involved. Its case is harder than metal in order to enable it to survive the fall. But therein lies the danger. How will the seed ever escape its metallike prison? Even if it could find some means of exiting from its encasement, it would need to find some means of transportation to enable it to be planted in hospitable and fertile soil. How can all this be arranged?

To many animals, the Brazil nut has little attraction. It has no smell, and it is too tough a nut to be cracked. No

Without the agouti, the Brazil nut would not exist.

doubt most animals are not even aware that it contains anything edible. How should they — they have not read this article! But there is hope — in the shape of an animal called the agouti. The agouti is a rodent the size of a large rabbit that trots nervously through the forest undergrowth on long thin legs. Its front teeth are chisel sharp and fully capable of cutting through the capsule and the shells of the nuts within to reach the rich fruit that they contain. But a single capsule produces 20 or so nuts, far more than an agouti can eat at a single sitting. Rapidly, it gathers them into its special cheek pouches. One by one, it takes them away, digs a little hole with feverish movements of its little front feet, drops the nut in and then covers it up, carefully stamping the earth down afterwards to conceal the site from its rivals. Back and forth it scampers until all the nuts have been hidden. Now it will be able to retrieve them at a later date.

Fortunately for the bertholletia tree, the agouti's memory is not perfect. A considerable proportion of the nuts that it hides, it never finds again. Happily for the tree, those hidden nuts will grow to produce new generations. (Interestingly enough, another creature, a bird called the nutcracker, performs the same favor for the pine tree. The pine tree takes two years to develop its seeds. During this long time they are kept safe within hard woody cones, where they are of little interest to animals. But when they are ready, the segments of the cones open and the seeds fall out. The nutcracker is just as prudent as the agouti, and does its best to hide those seeds it cannot eat immediately. And its choice of hiding place could not be better as far as the pine tree is concerned. The nutcracker always buries the seeds in open areas away from shade. That is just the sort of site that suits the seedling, and much preferable to one in the shade of other adult pines. The depth at which the nutcracker buries the seeds *exactly* matches the seeds' needs — not so shallow that other hungry animals will easily find them, and not so deep that the seedling will have difficulty in pushing up through the soil to the light. Fortunately for the pine tree, the nutcracker's memory is no better than the agouti's. Two out of every three seeds the bird buries, it never finds again.)

Reading something like this makes you think. Without the help of the agouti, the Brazil nut's parent tree would find it difficult to spread its seeds, on which survival depends. Without Brazil nuts, the agouti would be a hungry little rodent. Without its specially designed chisel-teeth, the agouti would be as helpless as we are without a nutcracker. Without a cheek pouch, it could not perform its job of transporter. How do they know where to plant them? What would happen if the agouti's memory was infallible, in which case no nuts would be forgotten underground to sprout into new trees? How does the bertholletia manage to produce a nut case that is stronger than any human teeth from raw materials that are liquid and gas (soil, water, carbon dioxide and sunshine)? Just how does it know how strong animal teeth are? There is powerful evidence of an amazing coordination by a Great Intelligence, Who also designs and creates everything in one Master plan.

As a general rule, anything that is well protected is precious. The rule that applies to money in the bank, the human heart and brains, applies equally to nuts. The fact is that nuts contain an enormous amount of goodness, not only for animals, but also for humans. You might have heard that eating fish is good for the brains. The reason is that fish are high in the trace mineral *selenium*, and there is evidence to suggest that people who **skimp** on selenium are more likely to suffer the blues. Psychologists David Benton and Richard Cook at University College in Swansea, Wales, recently documented that people eating the least selenium were the most anxious, depressed and tired, and generally felt much better when they received adequate selenium.

Receiving such information might depress you or make you feel anxious, wondering where you might procure the precious trace mineral! Worry no longer. Most selenium in the diet comes from grains, fish and cereals. But the king of selenium is the Brazil nut. The Brazil nut is the richest of all foods in selenium, and eating a single nut each day will guarantee that you are never deficient. Brazil nuts, because they are grown in selenium-rich soil, are superhigh in the mineral — about 2,500 times as selenium rich as any other nut.

But Brazil nuts are not the only nuts in the world. All of the species in creation are rich in goodness. (Do beware of peanuts [which are technically not nuts], which can be a prime cause of acute allergic reaction in susceptible individuals). Walnuts and almonds help reduce cholesterol and contain high concentrations of the antioxidant oleic acid. What exactly are oxidants? Oxygen, besides being a life-giving gas, has toxic forms too. Understand it this way: Renegade oxygen molecules called oxidants, and the body's police force, called antioxidants, are in constant combat. If walnuts and almonds are rich in antioxidants, especially vitamin E, it means that they put into your body the substances that strive to protect cells by fending off the destructive oxygen molecules.

Another remarkable ingredient present in nuts is the trace mineral *boron*. Lack of boron can downshift the brain's performance, making people just that bit slower. It is a remarkable fact that the brain is subject to fine-tuning by minute amounts of a food constituent. (Anyone who has experienced the soporific effect of *cholent* on Shabbos will not be surprised!) Since nuts, as well as fruit (in particular, apples, pears, peaches and grapes), are high in boron, eating just a small quantity each day can have a healthy stimulating effect on the brain. In addition, eating a few nuts each day can act as a powerful antidote to heart disease. Nuts have been shown to protect against chest pains and artery damage. Nuts are rich in fiber and olive-oil type fats, which are also known to counteract heart disease. Nuts, and also peanuts, are good regulators of insulin and blood sugar, preventing steep rises, making them good food for those with glucose intolerance and diabetes.

The humble nut, inside its amazingly impregnable nut case, is precious indeed. Healthy and nutritious, cheap and available, it humbly offers eloquent evidence of a Great Benefactor, Who with foresight and design is the only One able to condense so much good into such a small space.

An Illuminating Tale

Do you sleep enough? There is a popular saying in *yeshivah* circles that "Adam muad l'olam," which literally means that a human being possesses the potential for committing damage; but idiomatically means that people are always tired. If you are in the category of humans who are constantly suppressing yawns, prefer to sit down during the reading of the Torah because it gives you the opportunity for an unofficial rest, and carefully position yourself behind someone with a broad back during any *derashah* knowing that within five minutes your chin will be resting comfortably on your chest — then you don't have to blame yourself. The ones to blame are two men: an Englishman, Joseph Swan, and an American, Thomas Alva Edison. Both these gentlemen, working independently at first, invented the electric light bulb. It is the electric light bulb that has changed the face of society, and enabled people to turn night into day, "burn the midnight oil," stay up too late, subsequently staggering through the day bearing the burden of fatigue.

Every day, we switch on lights without too much thought. Yet the electric light bulb, which was to transform cities and bring safe light into every home, was invented less than 120 years ago. Both Swan and Edison, working on opposite sides of the Atlantic, had the same idea of passing a current through a "filament," or thread of cotton which had been scorched to form carbon. The filament glowed when the current was switched on. Sometimes the carbon burned through too quickly, and sometimes the glass bulb containing the filament broke. But, by 1880, both men had developed efficient, lasting bulbs. Edison had a natural flair for publicity, and had streetlights installed in his home town of Menlo Park, New Jersey. By 1882, his bulbs were lighting an area of New York City. Eventually, Edison and Swan joined forces, forming the Edison and Swan United Electric Light Company. Their pioneering work led to the "all-electric" homes of today. Have a look at your ceiling — is there a light burning? Do you stay up too late at night reading by the glow of electric lights? Thank, or blame, the bright inventiveness of Messrs. Edison and Swan.

No one, however tired they may be, will deny that the two inventors were extremely clever men. Had they decided to spend their evenings watching television (which would have been difficult, since television relies on electricity) instead of applying their intelligence, the world would have remained a darker place. But animals got there first. There are numerous species of animals that have the ability to communicate by using light.

The tiny firefly uses its light for signaling. The system is not unlike the Morse code, as once used by naval signalers when working with hand lamps, except that the fireflies' version is much more complicated. Morse uses just two kinds of flashes, one short and one long. Firefly flashes vary considerably in length, some lasting for as much as five seconds, and others being repeated 40 times within a single second at a speed so swift that human eyes are unable to perceive the intervals between them. In the United States, fireflies operate individually. There are several different species often occupying the same meadow or woodland. The males are much smaller than the females, and outnumber them by as many as 50 to 1. Finding an unattached female is an extremely competitive business.

The display starts soon after sunset, and lasts for an hour or so. The females emerge from their burrows while the males cruise through the air flashing their presence, each species using its own characteristic code. One produces long bursts at the rate of a flash every half-second. Another makes two flashes a second apart and then stops and waits. A third makes only single sporadic flashes. The most common response from the females of all species is a single short flash, but the time they allow to elapse before making their response is critical, and a searching male will not take notice of a reply unless it comes at the correct time interval after he has concluded his call.

It is an amazing thing. Curving trails of colored light help to attract customers into a fairground. The colored signals of the diminutive insects are performing the same function. The difference is that the fairground requires a generator and energy consumption (usually diesel) to produce its effect, while the glowworm or firefly achieves it chemically and without effort. In fact, the "fire" of the fireflies is a misnomer, for the light they produce is cold, and in energy terms, remarkably efficient. Whereas most electric bulbs waste 97 percent of their energy in heat (just place your hand over a reading lamp), a firefly concentrates 90 percent of its effort into light.

How does it do it? A complex protein called *luciferin,* when mixed with small quantities of an enzyme called *luciferaze,* will combine with oxygen and in the process give off a bright glow. The luciferin is stored behind areas of transparent cuticle backed by dense tissue that acts as a reflector. The glow emerging from so tiny an animal, though scarcely dazzling, is sufficient to read a printed page. Indigent Japanese students, too poor to afford other lighting, it is said, used fireflies to illuminate their nocturnal studies, and in parts of South America, the flies were enclosed in perforated gourds for domestic lighting.

A light that cannot be switched off can be more of an impediment than an advantage. A female North American firefly, as she comes in to land, flashes her tail-light with increasing frequency until, just before touchdown, her flashes fuse into a continuous glow. As soon as she comes to a halt, she switches off entirely. The common European glowworm who frequents damp hedgerows and meadows is most active in June and July, when the wingless females ascend tall grass stems and hang head down, twisting their bodies to expose the greenish lanterns under their tails. The winged males can pinpoint this tiny signal from at least 100 yards away, though if alarmed, the female can switch off the light at will. Anyone who lives near an airport will see planes approaching the runway at night. Powerful beams of light mounted on the wings cut through the gloom on the plane's descent. When the plane has come to a complete stop, and passengers are reminded to take all their personal belongings with them, the lights are dimmed. All the intelligence that has been utilized in the construction of the plane dims into insignificance when compared to the intelligence demonstrated by the diminutive creatures of Creation.

Listen to this amazing event. In New Zealand, there is an insect called a fungus gnat that uses light to attract its prey. Its larvae (the juvenile stage between hatching and adulthood in those species of animals in which the young have a different appearance and way of life from the adults) live in many places — beneath bridges, under the overhangs of damp sheltered banks, within hollow trees — but they are most famous for gathering in millions within caves. Each of them secretes a tube of clear mucus which it suspends horizontally from the ceiling of the cave and within which it lives. From this it hangs several dozen threads, each beaded with globules of sticky, adhesive glue. As it sits within its translucent home, it glows with a steady unblinking light so that the whole ceiling shines like the Milky Way. The light attracts midges and moths, which become entangled in the threads. The larvae above, when they sense the vibrations caused by the trapped insects, bite a hole through their tube and haul up the thread with their mandibles (lower jawbones, like fishermen reeling in their catch. Try working out how many separate inventions there are in that little story.

The following is not for the fainthearted, There is a species of fish called an angler fish. When they are hungry, which is often, they wave a luminous bait on a "fishing rod" which is strategically positioned above their open jaws. The luminous lure is cast ahead in the way a fisherman casts his line. When some curious fish closes in to investigate, the lure is drawn gently back towards the angler's mouth. Its lower jaw suddenly drops down, and the gill covers expand, exposing a cavity easily able to engulf prey that is actually larger than the angler fish itself.

The angler fish is not alone. As well as having a luminous tip on the end of its long dorsal fin, a viperfish has rows of lights along its sides and 300 more light organs inside its mouth. Its snakelike body gives it a fine burst of speed (!) and it rushes upon its victims with jaws agape. Bedazzled and bemused by the sudden glare of lights, the poor victims stay immobile long enough to be impaled on the viperfish's forward-pointing fangs.

Edison and Swan utilized their not inconsiderable intelligence to invent the electric bulb. The illuminating examples of lights found in the animal world indicate even greater intelligence. The question is: From where does all that intelligence come? Certainly not from themselves. Try and grow a light bulb from your head. Try really hard! The larvae of the fungus gnat is just a little less intelligent than you and its life depends on its luminous stunt, and its expert knowledge of glue. How did it manage it? Who told the insects about luciferin and luciferaze? Who taught them chemistry? The answer is that intelligence does not come from nowhere. It has a source. And that source is the greatest Intelligence of all.

The House That Jack Built

E nthusiasm is never a substitute for expertise. Recently, a young man went on vacation to Switzerland. Beautiful place, Switzerland, with mountains peppered across the whole country. Every corner you turn, there is another Alp, and the whole place looks like a picture postcard come true. Well, this young man looked out of his hotel window, and saw a few small-scale Alps rising from the edge of the village. Being newly arrived in Switzerland, he decided it would be a good idea to climb to the top of the nearest mountain and return in time for supper. It did not look too high, and most of the mountain was covered with fir trees. It was only the top bit that was bare and rocky, but on the whole the climb seemed quite possible.

He put on his brand-new climbing boots, told no one where he was going (why should he, it was just a short way to the top and back), and set off. Full of eagerness and enthusiasm, he began at a cracking pace, more running than walking. He did not bother looking for a path, but just climbed vertically. Very shortly, he noticed two things. First of all, the trees never ended. However far he climbed, there were always more trees stretching towards the horizon. Secondly, he was losing energy fast. After about half an hour's exertion, he was perspiring heavily, his heart was pounding, his legs were aching, and he was nowhere near any summit. He was surrounded by giant fir trees, all alone, exhausted, and then it began to rain. Dripping, energy spent, and cold, he decided that discretion was the better part of valor and turned back to base, wiser for the experience.

Imagine trying to build a house without any expertise, but lots of enthusiasm. Running up a mountain can result in a pair of sore feet and a bout of exhaustion, whereas a house built by amateurs will produce disaster. Pisa's famous leaning tower is a monument to the consequences of a small error in construction — imagine what a complete lack of expertise would produce. Not for nothing is there a group of professionals called architects. They spend five years or more studying methods of construction, and various types of building. They have to learn how to utilize wood, metal, concrete, glass and other materials necessary for building, and they have to be familiar with the installation of electricity, gas, water, drains, central heating and air conditioning.

If you were an architect, and wanted to design a building, you would first discuss with the client the nature of the building that he has in mind. Detailed plans and drawings would follow, all of which would have to be scrutinized and approved by local planning officers — professionals who are well experienced in the knowledge of the disasters that can

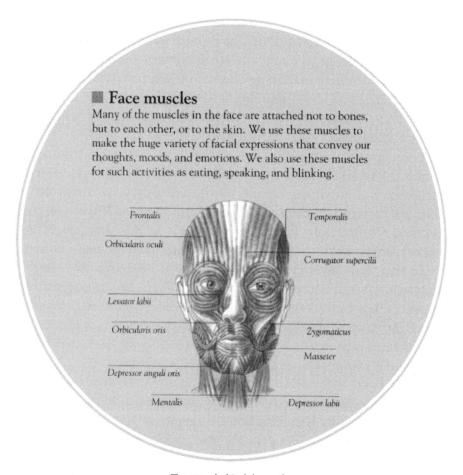

■ Face muscles

Many of the muscles in the face are attached not to bones, but to each other, or to the skin. We use these muscles to make the huge variety of facial expressions that convey our thoughts, moods, and emotions. We also use these muscles for such activities as eating, speaking, and blinking.

Frontalis

Temporalis

Orbicularis oculi

Corrugator supercilii

Levator labii

Orbicularis oris

Zygomaticus

Masseter

Depressor anguli oris

Mentalis

Depressor labii

The story behind the smile

occur when a structure is insufficiently planned. People sometimes think that the job of an architect is relatively simple — that an inspired few lines on the back of an envelope will translate into fame and fortune. Nothing could be further removed from reality. Our friend the architect is responsible for every minute detail in the proposed building — from the window frames to the roof slates, from the door handles to the bathroom fittings. It is he who will decide how the building will be heated, ventilated, and provided with water, gas and electricity. It is through his planning that windows will fit, doors will close, and the rain remain outside.

Enthusiasm let loose on a building site will produce a brick wall that rises and falls like the waves on the seashore; and is guaranteed to come crashing down just like a wave. It will never produce anything that is either functional, habitable or efficient. Enthusiasm without planning is fine for ambitious China's five-year economic plans, but it will not erect the simplest of garden fences.

There is a construction with which we are all intimately familiar. We use it in a multitude and variety of ways every single day of our lives. We rely on its efficiency, its durability and its versatility. Because of our familiarity with it, we often take it entirely for granted, which is a shame, for the construction which is so brilliantly planned is none other than our own body. The human body is an incredible masterpiece of bioengineering. Under its skin lie hundreds of muscles, bones, blood vessels, glands and other parts. These work day and night, as blood pulses through the arteries and veins, food passes through the intestines, and electrical signals flash along the nerves.

It is impossible not to be impressed with the human body. To the biologist, the body is built up from millions and millions of cells that help the body to grow and maintain itself. To the chemist, the body is an amazingly complicated combination of atoms and molecules, undergoing millions of chemical reactions every second. To the dietary expert, the body is a collection of substances — proteins, minerals, and carbohydrates — needing to take in correctly balanced types of food to keep itself in order. And to a mechanical engineer, the body is an incredibly sophisticated, self-controlling, self-repairing machine. Many science-fiction stories feature robots and other humanlike machines. It is highly doubtful if the technology needed to build such sophisticated machines will ever exist. Robots have never successfully copied the body's ability to walk in a well-balanced way on two legs, let alone its huge variety of fast action, precise movements and its range of sight, hearing, touch and other senses. Even the most advanced computers do not come close to the human brain's capacity for intelligent thought, learning and creativity. Every single aspect of the whole structure of the human body eloquently declares planning and foresight of the most detailed kind.

Take a few simple examples. Everyone's nose (as everyone knows) is directly above their mouth. The nose has three main functions. One is to inhale air, moisten and warm it, and send it down to the lungs. (The fact that the body is equipped with two independent methods of inhaling life-giving air, one through the mouth, the other through the nose, thus allowing an emergency route should one or the other become blocked, is not accidental and should not be ignored.) The second is to detect aromas, by means of the olefactory organ housed in the upper section of the nose. The third is to support the eyeglasses that permit millions of humans to see in focus. If you were planning the human body, you would suggest that it is important to be able to see the food as it approaches your mouth. Similarly, the aroma of the food greatly enhances the enjoyment of the eating process. Smelling the food requires the person to inhale (capturing flying molecules and delivering them safely to the olefactory organ). Seeing (in focus with the help of eyeglasses, nestling comfortably on the nose), smelling, and breathing are thus all integrated functions, requiring them to be in close proximity. Not surprisingly, they are.

The ideal way to breathe is through the nose. In that manner, the air is warmed (by passing through turbanates, which are heated by an enriched blood supply — the reason why a tap on the nose can produce such a volume of bleeding) and moistened. Breathing through the nose has the added advantage of allowing the nose owner to keep his mouth closed. Without that seemingly simple capability, it would be virtually impossible to drink liquid or chew food. It would just come gushing out. The nose cannot be shut, and ears cannot be sealed. There is no need. The mouth, whose digestive functions demand a waterproof barrier, has been provided with two lips, which, when sealed, allow no entry or exit. No matter how thick the moustache, not a single hair grows on the lips. They are soft and flexible, and permit Mr. Man to convert the raw sound produced by the voice box into meaningful sound.

The fact that parting the lips in a particular manner is a universally accepted gesture of friendship — and that the lips have this capability (you can't part your nose, ears or chin, however hard you try) — is remarkable. It would not be at all far-fetched to say that this is also a manifestation of the forward-planning with which the body is replete. The fact is that it would be impossible to pull the mouth corners up and out in the characteristic smile movement without a band of muscles called *zygomaticus*. Those muscles are anything but haphazard. They are anchored to the bony skull, and are activated by electrical impulse messages sent through the nerve system. The simple act of smiling is an electromechanical wonder, as complex as opening your metallic garage door with a remote-control radio transmitter.

Is there anything more natural than a yawn? It's a wonder. If you breathe slowly at rest, the lungs do not rid themselves of sufficient carbon dioxide, and it builds up in the blood. As the blood flows through the brain, a chemical message is delivered to the brain informing it that the carbon dioxide level is rising. Danger. The brain responds (electrical message) by triggering an extra deep breath, called a yawn. This "blows off" the excess carbon dioxide and brings in more oxygen.

Nothing at all in the human body is haphazard. Everything is preplanned and calculated in a manner that often defies our comprehension. Rushing up a mountain without thought results in failure. Building a brick wall without expertise will produce a pile of trouble and instant rubble. The human body?

Mi'bsori echezeh Kel.

Superglue – Superior Intelligence

L ife used to be simple. Once upon a time, if someone wanted two surfaces to stick together, he could find the necessary ingredients in his kitchen: flour and water; pure *chametz*, but reasonably effective to make two surfaces adhere together, as long as they were not thicker than a sheet of paper. However, if your mother-in-law was about to arrive for a visit, and you had just broken her favorite crystal vase (accidently), and wished to repair the damage, flour and water might not be advisable. Not if you wished to remain on good terms. For that you would need something a little more sophisticated.

It really is interesting. Until a century ago, glues were made either from gums from plants or from boiled-down hides and bones of animals. These gums and glues took a long time to firm up, and they formed a joint that was not particularly strong. Today, however, most glues are wholly synthetic. They dry quickly and form very strong bonds. The fastest-acting ones are called superglues and they set in seconds. Have you ever seen a car actually suspended in midair, attached to a billboard by epoxy resin glue? Not only that, it carries a second car on its roof — a powerful demonstration of the strength of glue. How does it work, and why doesn't it stick in the tube?

This really is clever. Superglue is an acrylic resin made from petroleum chemicals. When it is exposed to the slightest trace of moisture, the small molecules of the resin and the molecules of the surface bond together to form longer ones — a chemical process called *polymerization*. The two surfaces are now joined. In the tube, the glue is prevented from polymerizing by an acidic stabilizer. When it is applied to a surface, the most minute amount of moisture overcomes the action of the stabilizer, and the resin polymerizes instantly. The question is, though: Is there moisture on every surface? The answer is yes. It is the presence of water ions — groups of atoms that have an electric charge — that triggers off the polymerization process. The ions are present on practically any surface that is exposed to the air, because the air always contains some moisture.

But beware. Superglues stick well to skin because it is moist. There have been many cases of people becoming stuck to all sorts of objects from teacups to door handles. They can be freed by soaking the stuck part in warm water and gently pulling it away. Human intelligence has developed this mighty bond one stage further. Superglues have been used in surgery as an aerosol spray to seal wounds and reduce bleeding.

You can understand that human intelligence is able to collate knowledge; to scientifically investigate the chemical

Some glue! How did the insect think of it?

properties of substances; and exploit scientific advances for its own ends. Every time you pick up a tube of glue, you are benefiting from a mountain of accumulated intelligence. What would you say if all this knowledge was contained in a lowly creature which we would consider the very antithesis of intelligence? The creature? Read on!

A deadly night hunter moves slowly and silently across the damp leaf litter of a forest floor in Central America. (Another reason for choosing *Eretz Yisrael* for your vacation.) It is a type of velvet worm — *peripatus* — that hunts small creatures such as spiders, millipedes and insects. The longest and largest variety of this delightful species grows to some 6 inches in length. Each has a segmented body with many pairs of fleshy legs along the sides. Most of the legs end in little claws that are used to grasp slippery prey, but two pairs of legs are specialized tools. One pair has been set to form jaws with hard claws on the end, and the other pair to form a "gun" that shoots glue.

Although the worm moves slowly, this can be an advantage, because its stealthy approach allows it to draw near to its victim unnoticed. It often sets its sights on a cricket (creature, not the game) and unless the prey reacts quickly, it is struck by a 20-inch stream of glue. The struggling victim soon gets its legs stuck together, and if it continues to squirm, its captor generously immobilizes it with further squirts of glue. The glue, just like its tubular cousin, hardens on contact with air, forming a sturdy rope. With its prey subdued, the worm pierces a hole in the cricket with its clawlike jaws, and injects a lethal dose of saliva, which poisons the pray and begins to predigest it. Later, the worm feasts on its hard-earned supper. A large meal may satisfy the glue-gunner for up to a fortnight, but often it has to share the feast with scavengers that flourish on the jungle floor.

The glue-manufacturing worm is not profligate. It knows that glue is expensive ammunition. It is manufactured in the kidneys from protein, and each time the worm fires, it loses weight and energy. To conserve energy, the worm eats the rope as well as the prey, thus recovering as much of its expenditure as possible.

Glue as an effective weapon is not the monopoly of worms. There is another little creature, the tropical spitting spider that uses glue to capture its prey. This spider shoots out sticky streams from its jaws in a vigorous zigzag pattern, that quickly reduces its victim to a gummy immobile object. It is an action too fast for the human eye to follow — the spider simply seems to shake its head and the prey is immobilized instantly. What is interesting is that these spiders do not spin webs, but rely totally on their glue-shooting capabilities to capture their next meal. The glue is produced in small amounts in special glands, and so far no one has succeeded in discovering its chemical composition.

Many obvious questions spring to mind. Imagine that you needed glue for some domestic task, but the shops were closed. Better still, imagine that you were marooned on a desert island and there were no shops at all — and you needed glue. Could you inform your kidneys to produce some? Think of all the stages that the spider and the worm needed to master in order to be efficient in their hunting capabilities. They need a specialized, detailed knowledge of the scientific properties of glue. It is not sufficient to know that glue is sticky, but a precise knowledge of the molecular construction of chemicals, and how they react with other molecular construction of chemicals, and how they react with other molecular structures is needed. They need to know precisely the strength of glue necessary to trap their victims. Too weak a solution will be useless, and too powerful a concoction will waste precious materials. The worm and spider have to invent some method of shooting the glue at a distance with absolute accuracy. That requires a precise knowledge of pipes, valves, explosives, trajectories, gravity and hydraulics. The little spider and worm need to perfect a method to prevent the superglue from solidifying inside themselves, thereby committing themselves to a sticky end. At some stage, the spider has to decide to opt out of the web-weaving union and to concentrate on its glue production. How will it survive while one skill is being shut down, and the other still developing? Is there an International Fund for Struggling Spiders?

In order to function as effective glue-shooters, both the spitting spider and the velvet worm need to be expert in the field of molecular chemistry, electricity (the message to fire the glue-gun is transferred from the brain to the gun's firing mechanism by nerves, in itself an electrochemical wonder of dazzlingly complicated proportions), ballistics and zoology. To the best of anyone's knowledge, the spider and the worm know nothing about these complex subjects. The whole complicated apparatus has to work to perfection if it is to work at all. If any stage of the procedure would be deficient, both the worm and the spider would be long extinct. Logical thinking demands that there must be a Superior Intelligence that is in possession of all the technical information, capable of designing the whole apparatus.

One of the many complex systems at work within the human body on which our survival depends is the coagulation of blood. Within the body, blood must never coagulate. If a wound punctures the blood supply, the need for the blood to coagulate to prevent a fatal leak is vital. The fact that there is such a system in place is evidence of advance planning and the Greatest Intelligence, but it is immensely complicated. A veritable cascade of enzymes and proteins have to chain-react in precise sequence for the system to work. Again, it either works perfectly, or not at all. Imagine therefore, that a tiny tick, a form of mite, has all the knowledge at hand. A tick is a parasite that feeds on the blood of other creatures. Apart from a special chemical in its saliva that dissolves tissue, enabling the tick to embed its mouth in the victim's skin, its saliva also contains anticoagulant to prevent the blood from clotting while it feeds. Has the tick managed to master the complexities of blood coagulation to then produce an anti-coagulant? Do you really think so? Rather it is further compelling evidence of the work of a Supreme Intelligence that created everything with the greatest wisdom.

I f anyone would venture to claim that we are a spoiled generation, there is no use denying it. It's true. We have never had it so good, and still we find cause to complain. In the not-too-distant past, if someone wished to travel to Australia from Europe, the ocean liner was the only available mode of transport. In a journey lasting several weeks, no one would have thought of complaining if the voyage would have taken an extra day. (In those days, the longest day's run claimed by any sailing ship was one of 465 nautical miles, and that was in a northwesterly gale!) In today's sophisticated age, if the plane journey is delayed by one hour, the passengers feel aggrieved.

The single factor that has enabled journey time to tumble is the invention of the jet engine. In times gone by, when the crossing of the Atlantic took weeks, when the crew were as much in danger of starvation as they were from shipwreck, who could have dreamed that in the year 1974 (just 33 years after the advent of jet aircraft), U.S. Major James Sullivan would be able to cross the same stretch of water in just 1 hour and 54 minutes and 56.4 seconds at an average speed of 1806 mph?

It is an interesting fact that despite the great increase in the speed of air travel, or rather because of it, the maneuverability of aircraft has been much reduced. A pilot in the First World War, flying a Sopwith Camel at about 100 mph needed no less than 80 yards to turn in order to evade the machine guns of a German Fokker. Today's jet fighters fly at over 1500 mph, and their turning circles are so large — about 15 miles — that it is difficult for the opposing pilots to see each other at all. One particular plane, however, has the capability to give its pursuers some surprises, and that is the subsonic British Harrier aircraft. They can land and take off vertically, and a Harrier pilot can alter the angle of thrust of his engine during flight by swiveling the jets' discharge nozzles. This enables him to reduce speed by 200 mph in a few seconds, while at full throttle. A Mirage pilot who had been on the Harrier's tail would find that he was now in front, and vulnerable.

There is in the world today a flying machine that can outperform and outshine any contemporary jet aircraft. Its maneuverability is unsurpassed. It can change its direction of flight a full 180 degrees in a split second. It can detect hostile enemy action without the use of radar, and it can successfully land on a vertical surface or even upside down. This flying wonder — the humble fly — buzzes at the sunny windows, hovers hungrily over the dinner or outdoor table, and are so inevitably a part of warm-weather existence that most people resignedly take them for granted. This is a shame, for buzzing around is a creature that demonstrates

An unwelcome visitor to the kitchen but a briliant flyer

greater technical brilliance and futuristic design than the most advanced plane we are ever likely to encounter. The fact that flies get on our nerves should not prevent us from appreciating their remarkable capabilities, all of which point to remarkable design.

Our housefly starts life as a tiny egg, much smaller than a pinhead, deposited by the mother fly in any rotting refuse. There then follow a series of events, each more remarkable and breathtaking than the next. Within 24 hours, it hatches as a transparent legless grub. Before a day has passed, its size has so tremendously increased that its skin, which is not elastic, can no longer contain the body. The skin splits, and the grub crawls out to grow a new skin. Three times within as many days this splitting and shedding of old skins occurs, and then on the fourth day, its transparent color changes to a dull white, it crawls away from its feeding place, and burrows into the ground. During its underground existence of a further three days, there forms within its skin the striped body, the six legs, the two veined wings, the multi-faceted eyes — a tremendous metamorphosis for so short a time. Then the pupa bursts and the adult fly emerges. Tunneling upward, it comes out into the sunlight, ready for its eight to ten weeks of adult life. Put all that into the context of a constructed aircraft, and ask yourself if such an amazing process has any parallel!

What makes the housefly such a health hazard is its remarkable physique. Its prime concern is food. It relishes with equal enthusiasm decaying garbage and the lumps of sugar on the kitchen table — and it flies directly from one kind of food to the other. Its entire body is covered with a tangle of fine, close-growing hairs; and similar hairs grow on its legs and feet. The fly is thus equipped with the finest of shopping bags. In addition, each foot is equipped with an adhesive pad of sticky hairs. It is by means of these that the fly negotiates slippery surfaces so nimbly, and can walk upside down on ceilings; but it is also by means of these sticky pads that it picks up and transmits myriad germs. Another fascinating characteristic is the fact that houseflies do not have any chewing mechanism. Accordingly, a fly can feed on a lump of sugar only by softening it. To do this, the fly regurgitates a drop of fluid from its last-digested meal onto the sugar! Not for nothing do people say that if you would follow a fly on its varied journeys for a day, you wouldn't eat for a week!

Many people wonder why it is so difficult to swat a fly. It seems to be able to sense the imminent arrival of the towel from any angle. When you look into the wonders of the eyesight of the fly, it is hardly surprising. A typical fly has two compound eyes strategically placed at the front of its face, giving it complete all-round vision. Each eye is composed of more than 1000 tiny eyes — six-sided facets, each with its own lens and retina. (Humans have but two.) Through these compound eyes the fly sees a mass of images that together resemble a specked newspaper photograph. Each facet is stimulated successively by movement through its field of vision. This "flicker vision" enables the fly to detect even the tiniest of movements making it very difficult to catch. Since relative to its size, a man creeping up to a fly is as delicate as an elephant to a mouse, it is no wonder that the perceptive fly knows what's coming and skillfully bypasses the swinging towel.

Before an insect can take to the air, its body temperature has to be sufficiently elevated. Birds have an automatic mechanism for maintaining their body temperature (so do humans), but insects are affected by the air temperature for the rise and fall of their own body temperature. Flies disappear mysteriously when the sun goes behind a dark cloud. Larger insects make use of the metabolic heat generated by their flight muscles when they warm up by vigorously flapping their wings before takeoff. The humble bumblebee is capable of flight when conditions are only a degree or two above freezing by utilizing its specialized warming-up procedure, reaching an internal temperature of over 86 degrees Fahrenheit. For such a tiny creature to generate so much heat requires an enormous expenditure of energy. Even more remarkable is its ability to uncouple the flight muscles from its wings, vibrating and warming them up without actually moving its wings at all.

If so much energy is utilized in warming up the engine and in flying, there has to be some extraordinary means of storing that energy in the fly's body. (Modern planes store their fuel in the wings.) Insects' thorax (equivalent of the fuselage) contains many energy-storing tissues, of which the most remarkable is the wings' minute suspension system. This is made of *resilin*, the most perfect elastic material known, and one which has so far evaded man's attempts at synthesis. In addition, insects with high-frequency wing movements have an extraordinary muscle tissue known as *fibrillar* muscle. It is the most active tissue to be found in a living organism, having the peculiar quality of automatically contracting with great rapidity after being stretched. Once an impulse from the central nervous system initiates the system, the power supply for the wings continues running on its own until another nervous impulse stops it. Hence, the muscles can contract and relax far more rapidly than the nerves can fire them. With these mechanisms, many flies, bees and wasps are able to beat their wings at 200-250 cycles per second (one cycle is a complete up-and-down movement). The record beater is the tiny midge (*forcipomyia*) that beats its wings at an incredible 1,046 cycles each second.

Before landing, most insects extend their six legs out as soon as the landing surface comes within a few body lengths of them. The legs are designed to function as efficient shock absorbers, since, unlike aircraft and some birds, insects never run forward after touchdown. They arrive at their landing spot from almost any angle without slowing down at all. An idea of the efficiency of their landing gear is given by the estimates that some beetles are subjected to a force of about 40 times the force of gravity when they strike an unyielding surface — a force that would cause complete disintegration of any aircraft.

Move over, jet fighter. Stand aside, British Harrier. Let not our familiarity with the humble fly dull our recognition of features of design that outshine any plane. As sure as an aircraft indicates a wealth of design, the bluebottle fly with all its winged friends speaks volumes of the wisdom of the Greatest Designer of all.

Solar Panels in the Garden

L iving in the land of Israel is pleasant. Spiritual considerations aside, there are dimensions to the quality of life that other countries do not possess. Less fortunate people who inhabit colder, more northern countries are always struck by the warmth and the fragrance of Israel when they arrive at the airport. The sun shines brightly most of the year; daytime with its myriad activities begins earlier than the sleepy outreaches of Europe. And hot water is cheaper. The reason? Sunshine.

The energy that reaches the Earth in the form of sunlight

is immense — more than 12,000 times greater than the world's fuel consumption. The sunshine falling each year on the surface of America's roads alone contains twice as much energy as all the coal and oil used every year in the entire world. But collecting and storing this abundant supply of free energy is difficult and expensive. You cannot simply take a bucket, fill it with sunlight, and pour it into a sizable container! In domestic hot-water systems that use the sun's energy, solar collectors (panels) are mounted on roofs facing the sun. They have glass or plastic panels behind which water circulates in pipes painted black to absorb maximum heat. The heated water is then pumped into the hot-water tank. At least half the houses in Israel have solar panels strategically mounted on their roofs. They are also popular in California, but cloudier Europe, which gets only half the sunshine of Israel, has far fewer.

Solar energy has many everyday outlets. The "Solar Challenger," an airplane powered by 16,128 solar cells generating 2.5 kilowatts, crossed the English Channel in 1981. Solar cars carry batteries, but only to store solar energy for use when it is cloudy, or when the car is climbing hills. Solar-powered watches and calculators are widespread, and solar-heated swimming pools are becoming popular. (Isn't yours installed yet?) As every space explorer knows, virtually every spacecraft and satellite has depended on solar cells for its electricity since the U.S. satellite "Vanguard" in 1958. Solar cells exploit the discovery, made in 1887 by the German physicist Heinrich Hertz, that certain substances generate electricity when exposed to light — the photovoltaic effect.

There is little doubt that anyone viewing a solar panel for the first time, whether in Israel or any other country where the sun shines brightly, would be impressed by the technological feat. Whether the solar panel sits on the roof, or is installed as an integral part of the watch or calculator, no one would have difficulty in admitting that the combination of scientific knowledge and skill that produced such a useful invention is the result of intelligent design. A cursory glance

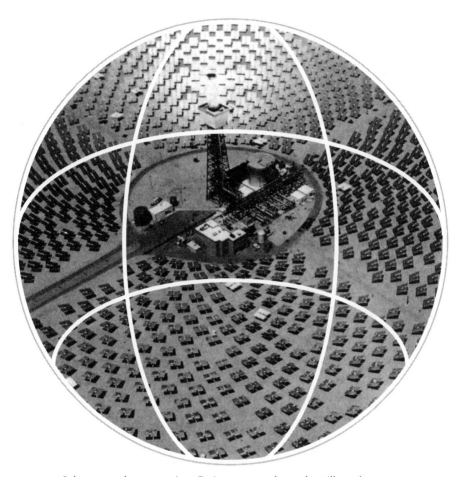

Solar-powered power station. Go into your garden and you'll see the same.

at that most common of plants — the green grass — will reveal a level of intelligent design that makes a solar panel appear as crude as a kettle on a fire by comparison.

Grass is green. Why? Because of a chemical substance, chlorophyll, which is found inside it. Chlorophyll performs a remarkable job, as will be explained. Ordinary white light, such as sunlight, is made up of different colors, or wavelengths. We don't normally see these colors unless the light is refracted (split into its constituent colors), as it is in a rainbow. Now, when light passes through chlorophyll, certain colors disappear. These colors are blue, and to a lesser extent, red. Blue and red disappear because they are absorbed by the chlorophyll. Other colors, particularly green, pass straight through it or are reflected. The reason why leaves look green is that chlorophyll reflects the green part of the spectrum.

Experiments show that the two colors that are best for photosynthesis (the process by which plants make food) are blue and red — the very same colors that are absorbed (surprise, surprise!). A plant which is deprived of these two colors cannot photosynthesize properly, and doesn't make the glucose that is later converted into starch. Sunlight provides these two colors in precisely the correct proportions.

Anyone wanting to know the exact size of the solar panels present in every blade of grass might be interested in the following information. If you would take a look at a simple (?) leaf under a microscope, you will see that its cells contain lots of small green bodies. These tiny things are called *chloroplasts,* and each one is filled with *chlorophyll.* It is in these tiny chloroplasts that the miracle called photosynthesis takes place. Chlorophlasts are extremely small. About 10,000 of them would fit onto the period at the end of this sentence. In terms of solar panels, that means constructing 10,000 individual solar panels, and sacking them in the space of a period, each of them interconnected, yet capable of functioning as an independent machine.

Each chloroplast is filled with rows of thin membranes. By careful analysis, it has been discovered that millions and millions of chlorophyll molecules are attached to these membranes. Every single molecule is a machine built to a specific design performing a vital and complex function! The chlorophyll molecules are laid out in a marvelous pattern, rather like the manner in which library books are stacked on shelves. In this way, a great many chlorophyll molecules are packed together in a small space. Think of a large tree. The tree has numerous leaves. Inside each leaf are numerous chloroplasts; within each chloroplast are numerous membranes; and covering each membrane are millions of chlorophyll molecules.

Each individual molecule has a vital task to perform, and each molecule is nothing less than a master chemist. Chlorophyll absorbs light energy and enables it to be used by the plant for building up sugar. Utilizing the most advanced chemical knowledge, the chlorophyll molecule combines light energy from the sun with water from the ground and carbon dioxide from the atmosphere, and produces oxygen and sugar. The sugar is then stored in the plant in the form of starch. In a remarkable experiment, a lighted candle was placed in a sealed chamber. As you can imagine, after a while, it was extinguished. A sprig of mint was then introduced into the chamber without any air being let in. The plant in the chamber was then left in the light. After about 10 days, the candle, on being lit, burned again. From where did the oxygen come? From the sprig of mint. There is a plant called *Canadian pondweed* that is even more dramatic. When placed in strong light, this plant actually produces bubbles of oxygen. Humans need oxygen to breathe, and plants require carbon dioxide to help in the production of their food. There is nothing more pleasant than living in a verdant tree-filled neighborhood, where the air is oxygen enriched; and nothing more foolish and criminal than destroying the forests that produce much of the oxygen that we all require.

It is indeed fascinating. A solar panel does nothing other than focus the light of the sun onto a water tank, in order to heat it. There is no chemical reaction, or combining of substances. Yet everyone is convinced of the intelligent design of the solar panels. We look for, and find, the manufacturer's name and country of origin. Each of the trillion molecules of chlorophyll contained in a single leaf does much more than focus light. Leaves are the food factories of a plant. The raw materials they use are the simplest: carbon dioxide, water, and a few mineral ingredients. The first, a gas, is all around them in the air, and they absorb it through tiny pores in their surface. (A pore is no accident. The Channel Tunnel that connects Britain to France is nothing but a pore, and is also no accident.) Water, and the minerals dissolved in it, are collected by the roots from the ground in which the plant grows. How do you collect water absorbed in earth? The roots of the plant seem to know the secret. The chemists within the tissues of the leaves that process the raw materials are the miracle molecules, chlorophyll. Sugars and starches are masterfully produced from sunlight, air and water. The by-product is oxygen, the gas that drifts away through the leaf pores (leaves breathe just like you and I) into the atmosphere to the benefit of every living creature.

A solar-cell power station, converting sunlight into electricity, was completed in California in 1981. It is a remarkable example of man's ability to harness natural resources to produce clean energy, and in an era that concerns itself greatly with protecting the environment, it offers great hope for the future. A vast circle of mirrors collects the sun's rays and reflects them onto a collection cell in the center of the mirrors. The heat produces steam to generate electricity, sufficient to supply the power for 20,000 people — a remarkable achievement. All of that, and more, contained in every humble blade of grass and innocuous leaf? Remarkable indeed. You don't have to go to the Alps to see the wonders of the Creator. Just take a glance at your garden, and see the masterfully designed solar panels, and there you will find the Creator of All.

The Computers Within

Once upon a time, there were no computers. Anyone wanting to add up numbers either used their hands, or, if the calculation exceeded 10, used an abacus. An abacus works by moving beads across a wire frame. The first mechanical calculator was patented in 1647 by Blaise Pascal of France, when he was only 24 years old. It had a system of interlocking rotating cogwheels. A definite improvement! The ultimate calculating machine was Charles Babbage's analytical engine, designed in the 1830s, replete with cogs and levers, but never built. Babbage was a professor at Cambridge, England. His machine could in theory perform all kinds of mathematical calculations, and it was the forerunner of the modern computer.

And then there were computers. The first electronic computers were a far cry from the powerful desktop machines of today. They weighed tons, and had a memory capacity of just a few numbers and letters. The first computer, built between 1942 and 1946, had a tiny memory. It was also very unreliable, because it contained around 18,000 bulky valves, which looked rather like lamp bulbs. These tended to overheat, and often needed replacing. But it was a start. The very first computer could add two numbers in 0.2 milliseconds, meaning that it could do in one day calculations that would take a human mathematician a year. The great leap forward came with the invention of the transistor. This provided a smaller replacement for the valve, and one which did not heat up. Suddenly, computers became smaller and more reliable, and the modern "information age" had truly begun.

And now? You don't have to be a technical whiz kid to understand that computers are complex, but logical. They also incorporate the greatest advances in technology. Take, for example, the computer's memory. Although it is as thin as a hair, and no bigger than a shirt button, a memory chip can hold around 450,000 electronic devices linked by circuit connections so fine that it would take 59 million to fill a one-inch thickness. In order to understand anything about the workings of a computer, you have to be aware of the astonishing qualities of the silicon chip, which carries the electric signals; and the fact that all messages, commands and calculations are converted to binary numbers (the system that uses only two digits; 0 and 1).

There is no rational mind in the world that would accept that the relatively primitive abacus was anything but designed. Not even the most radical skeptic would accept that the machines invented by Pascal and Babbage were anything but the results of innovative intelligence. Move on to contemporary computers, and there the intelligence that underlies their operation is so complex that the average hu-

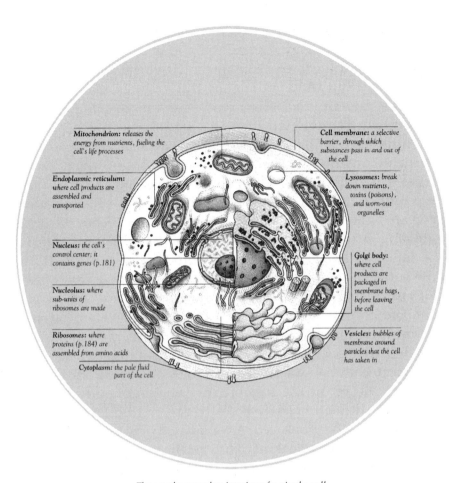

The vastly complex interior of a single cell

Labels in the figure:

Mitochondrion: *releases the energy from nutrients, fueling the cell's life processes*

Cell membrane: *a selective barrier, through which substances pass in and out of the cell*

Endoplasmic reticulum: *where cell products are assembled and transported*

Lysosomes: *break down nutrients, toxins (poisons), and worn-out organelles*

Nucleus: *the cell's control center; it contains genes (p.181)*

Golgi body: *where cell products are packaged in membrane bags, before leaving the cell*

Nucleolus: *where sub-units of ribosomes are made*

Ribosomes: *where proteins (p.184) are assembled from amino acids*

Vesicles: *bubbles of membrane around particles that the cell has taken in*

Cytoplasm: *the pale fluid part of the cell*

man mind cannot grasp it, and is content to benefit from the advanced technology, and leave the detailed knowledge to the experts.

We marvel at the complex machines and sophisticated devices of our modern world. We are space aged, technology obsessed, information rich and computer crazy. Yet the most wonderful machine in the Universe is right here with us now. We spend so much time gazing out of it that we rarely pause to look inward. If we would, we would find more to impress us than the most superadvanced electronic machine.

Take the smallest part of the human body, the cell. The human body is made of more than 50 billion billion cells. If you would take 40 cells and place them in a single line, the line would stretch all of one millimeter. However, the line would be only one cell wide, and far too thin to see. Cells are mostly water, and almost transparent — and more complex than anyone can possibly imagine.

Things do not float about at random inside a cell. Every cell is highly organized. It has a complicated set of inner structures, based on sheetlike membranes. In the same way that the body is made of major parts called organs, the parts of a cell are called *organelles*. Just like walls and floors divide a building into rooms, membranes divide the cell into hundreds of different compartments and chambers. The membrane on the outside is like an outer skin. Inside there are dozens of additional membranes forming the organelles. Some are spread out, folded and stacked in piles. Others are coiled and twisted to form the roomlike compartments. Still others form shapes like balls, balloons and sausages which contain stores of useful chemicals, or waste for disposal. Cell chemicals pass through "doors" in the membranes between organelles. They also pass through holes or pores in the main-cell membrane, into and out the whole cell. A cell is a city, no less.

Even the watery looking parts of the cell, called the *cytoplasm,* are not empty. They contain microtubules and microfilaments, which are the cell's inner scaffolding. They give strength and shape. Then comes the biggest wonder of all: the cell's control center. It is here, in the *nucleus,* that all the information and instructions to keep the cell alive and functioning are contained. The information the cell needs is in the form of immensely long coils of chemicals. These are known as *DNA.* It was only in 1953 that two scientists, Francis Crick and James Watson, discovered the structure of DNA.

What is this DNA, about which we hear so much? A cell is composed of many atoms, grouped together in molecules. A molecule is the smallest part of a substance that can normally exist by itself. DNA is an acronym for *deoxyribonucleic acid,* and is a molecule shaped like a corkscrew, rather like two spiral staircases wound round each other. DNA contains four chemicals linked in pairs — adenine and thymine, cytosine and guanine. The double spiral of these four chemicals that comprises the double spiral has rungs joining the two spirals. These rungs, or steps, consist of one of these two pairs of chemicals. (In short, A,T,C and G.) The order of the pairs varies — and that is the key. It is like varying the order of the letters in the alphabet when you write out words and sentences. So, DNA is a chemical version of a written instruction book, although the DNA alphabet has only four letters, unlike 26 in the alphabet you are reading now.

The whole "DNA Book" contains the information for building and running a living thing. Each and every type of living organism — an amoeba, a gnat, seaweed, a daisy, an oak tree, a human being — has its own DNA book, contained in the cell's nucleus. A *gene* is like a sentence in the book. It gives an instruction on how to build one of the thousands of molecules in the body, such as the protein called *keratin* in the skin, or the red blood cells. In total, there are probably between 100,000 and 200,000 genes (sentences) in the DNA Book for a human body. They are not strung along one enormously long DNA molecule, but are packaged like the separate volumes which make up one multivolume book. Now listen to this. Every single cell in the body (and remember that there are 50 billion billion cells in the body) has, inside its nucleus, the entire set of volumes, containing all 100,000-200,000 genes. Cells become different in their shapes, activities, functions and products because only some of their genes are switched on and working.

The comparison between a computer — with its binary code and memory capability — and the living cell — with its four-chemical code and vast volumes of information contained in a space so small that it is invisible to the human eye — becomes more apparent the more one observes. There is, however, one feature in the cell that no computer in the world can master. The ability to replicate itself. A machine such as a tape recorder needs its batteries to be replaced often. A portable computer also needs its batteries renewed. The body does it itself. Does it have to replace cells often? On average, about 3,000 million cells in the body cease to function every minute. They are replaced by 3,000 million new cells made by cell division. (The only exceptions are the nerve cells in the brain, which fade out at the rate of 10,000 each day and are not replaced. But don't worry, we all have an enormous amount of spare capacity!)

If we are discussing wonders, this possibly is the greatest wonder of them all. A cell, in a process called *mitosis,* has the ability to divide. Without this ability the body could not be maintained or grow. The DNA information library is housed in the cell's nucleus, packaged into structures called *chromosomes.* When the cell is ready to divide, the chromosomes duplicate themselves. The two sets then separate, each moving to one end of the cell. The cell membrane grows through the middle of the cell, splitting it in two. So two complete new cells, each with an identical full set of instructions, are formed from one parent cell. Cell division happens incredibly fast for some cell types. New red cells for the blood are produced at the rate of two million — every second of your life. Other cells are much longer lived, especially the nerve cells in the brain and the main nerves. This is because the intricate pattern of connections and links between the nerve cells would be disturbed if they ceased functioning too often. And the pattern of links and connections allows us to think and remember.

To think and remember, that there is a direct parallel between the functioning of a cell and the intricate construction of the computer. Except that the cell far surpasses the most advanced computer. The more we ponder, the more we see the magnificently complex wonders and design that formulate the "simple" cell. Think about it, and the evidence of a Creator speaks for itself.

In the olden day, soldiers who went to war were protected by heavy cumbersome suits of armor. In the days of the knights, his chief target during a conflict was the head of his foe, so special care was taken to protect the head with a helmet. All closed helmets had slits so that the wearer could see and breathe. Dressed in this fashion, the knight's own mother would not have recognized him, and he himself was not able to tell if he was fighting friend or foe! If not for the emblem that they fixed on their helmet, no one would have known whose head they were trying to knock off. Dressed like a human tank, the virtually immobile warrior made an easy target for enemy marksmen.

No longer. The modern soldier is professional, well trained, motivated, and equipped with a frightening array of super-sophisticated weaponry. On his head he will wear a combat helmet, with outstanding ballistic protection, designed with recesses for a radio headset. His jacket (known in the trade as "webbing") will incorporate quick-release buckles and easy-to-operate pouches. In addition, he will be issued layered body protection, camouflaged fleece jacket, and fully waterproof outer jacket. And don't forget the boots. His combat boots will provide a high level of comfort, allied to durability and perfect waterproofing, and with laces that don't tear.

Our modern soldier is not expected to carry his equipment in a shopping bag. Nor does the army wish him to lug his bed around in a wheelbarrow. On arrival at the recruitment center he is equipped with a large ergonomically designed rucksack, an excellent sleeping bag with waterproof cover, personal entrenching tool, warm combat gloves and sleeping bag. Being so perfectly dressed, the army authorities would hardly want their soldiers to fight with peashooters. Therefore, they come equipped with the very latest in mortars and rifles, machine guns and armored vehicles that technology can produce. The modern soldier enters the army in civilian clothing, and marches off to war fully dressed and equipped to perform his task as part of a highly professional, well-trained fighting force. Citizens of the country would wish for nothing less.

Such remarkable weaponry and equipment, designed as it is with care, foresight and wisdom, is commonplace in the created world. Take the cheetah as an example. When it comes to chasing prey, there is nothing that can beat the cheetah. With its slim, streamlined body, small head, long legs and supple spine, it is superbly shaped for swift bursts of speed. The cheetah's acceleration is simply astonishing. Like an arrow from a bow, it shoots forward from standstill to 45 mph in three seconds nearly as fast as a Formula 1 racing

"Nice pussy ... HELP!"

car, and faster than most sports cars. At full speed, the cheetah can reach 63 mph, faster than any other animal on earth.

The secret of the cheetah's amazing speed lies in the flexing and extending of its supple spine, allowing it to greatly
increase the length of its stride. As its spine arches to an astonishing extent, its hind legs can reach a long way
forwards, and then, when its spine extends, it increases the
forward reach of the front legs as well as adding pressure to
the backward thrust of the hind legs. This spinal flexing
gives the cheetah a stride of about 23 feet (compare this to
a single step of a knight in armor) — enough to make the

difference between success and failure in the chase.

The big cat's tremendous acceleration is augmented by the grip of its claws; they cannot be fully retracted, and act like the spikes on a sprinter's shoes. It would seem impossible for the cheetah to keep its eye on its target as it bounds through the air. (Try fixing your glare on an object while jumping up and down!) But, like a gun on a modern battle tank, which holds its aim however rough the ride, the cheetah can keep its head steady because of the great flexibility of its shoulders. That, and the narrow strip of concentrated light-sensitive cells fitted across the retina of each eye, enable it to clearly distinguish its intended prey from the details of the background.

Wanting to do something will not make it happen. Men have enviously observed birds flying through the air for a long time, wishing that they could be the ones that defy the laws of gravity with such grace and aplomb. The many brave chaps who have stood on high places with artificial wings strapped to themselves, and jumped, furiously flapping their arms, have not survived to write autobiographies. Wanting to be a bird will not grow you wings or give you an aerodynamic shape. An ardent desire to capture prey will neither produce nonretractable claws nor will it design a supple spine. Many people would dearly love to see in sharp focus. None of them have succeeded in growing an extra area of light-sensitive cells on their retinas. These things do not happen by themselves, and they do not happen slowly. The equipment has to be there when it is needed, just like the soldier.

Travel now from the East African plains to the eastern Australian outback. There you will see the famous bolas spider catching courting moths by spinning a slender silken thread with a sticky ball on the end — rather like the bolas used by gauchos, the cowboys of the South American pampas. The spider flavors the sticky ball with a chemical cocktail that smells like a female moth. The trap set, the spider suspends itself by a silken trapeze with the bolas dangling from one leg, and settles down to wait.

When male moths, drawn by the scent, come close enough for the spider to sense the beat of their wings, it whirls its deadly lure. The moths are caught fast on the sticky little ball, and hauled in to be eaten. Why does the moth not simply fly off, breaking the silken thread? No chance. The strand of spider silk, 250 times finer than a human hair, is twice as strong as steel. Indeed, the U.S. Air Force is exploring how the qualities of spider silk might be applied to bulletproof vests. Indeed, there is much to learn from the humble spider.

But from whom did the bolas spider learn? Who were the *Rebbis* that taught it how to produce steel thread from its own body? This is important information, because there are many mountain climbers in the world today keen to adapt their right index fingers to spin and unravel limitless lengths of high tensile rope while ascending and descending dizzying heights. They would be burning with curiosity to discover how to manufacture steel thread from raw materials of pizza and french fries. And then who told the spider what female moths smell like? Did the spiders conduct a survey among the moth population, clipboards under their many legs, jotting down the vital information? And how do you manufacture an aroma? If you, human readers, enjoy the scent of oranges, and wished to resemble an orange, at least in aroma, how would you set about smelling like an orange without going to live in Jaffa?

You do not have to be as fast as the cheetah to subdue your prey. As slow as a worm is also acceptable, given the right weaponry. As we discussed previously, the velvet worm, which operates in the forests of Central America, has many pairs of legs running the length of its body. One pair of legs culminates to form jaws with hard claws on the end, and another pair forms a gun that shoots glue. Although the worm moves slowly, this can be an advantage, because its stealthy approach allows it to approach its next meal unnoticed. Once supper is in sight (it might be an unsuspecting cricket), the velvet worm shoots a 20 inch stream of glue. The struggling victim soon finds itself in a sticky situation, and if it continues to squirm, its captor stills it with more squirts of glue. The glue hardens in contact with the air (not, you will notice, inside the worm) forming a sturdy rope.

The kindly worm then pierces a little hole in the insect with its specially designed clawlike jaw, and injects a lethal dose of saliva, which poisons the prey and begins to predigest it. Glue is also used by tropical spitting spiders to capture their insect prey. They shoot out sticky streams from their jaws in a vigorous zigzag pattern, that quickly inhibits the victim's movements. It is an action too fast for the human eye to follow — the spider simply seems to shake its head and its prey is immobilized instantly. The glue is produced in special glands in very small amounts, and so far, no one has succeeded in discovering its chemical composition.

Which is a shame, for such a discovery could earn a fortune! Every army in the world would give anything to provide their soldiers with the means to shake their heads and glue up their opponents. Why not ask the velvet worms, intelligent creatures that they are, how they do it? The simple answer is that in just the same way that a human has never succeeded in adapting his nose to become a mortar-launcher, or his right arm to become an automatic machine gun (and humans are the most intelligent of creatures), similarly the humble worm has never had the capability of adapting anything to its highly complex and sophisticated chemical discharger. Where does it all come from? A Higher Intelligence? Indeed.

The Toothbrush

These days, most homes are equipped with bathrooms. Despite the enormous variety of baths, in size, shape and color that make every bathroom unique, there is one commodity that is common to every single bathroom. The object in question is small, unassuming, costs little, but we couldn't manage without it. Its name? The toothbrush. The toothbrush lives in its own little stand, sometimes poking its head furtively out of the cup. When new, its bristles are proud and long, straight and strong. Gradually, as it ages, its head bends and slowly the bristles fall. Young or old, the ubiquitous

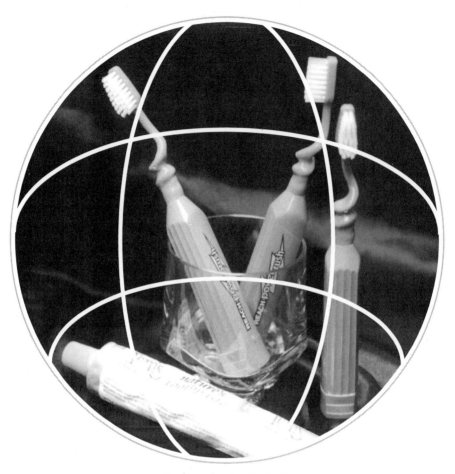

Machines for cleaning teeth

toothbrush is everybody's friend. You want your smile to be bright and white — use the toothbrush regularly. Brush your teeth twice every day; in your mouth they are sure to stay.

The toothbrush is such a common bathroom feature that it is rarely noticed except when it is missing. "Has anyone seen my toothbrush?" Need a new one? Off you go to your toothbrush store. The shelves are stocked with toothbrushes of every style and choice of quality. Hard, soft, over there, "approved by dentists everywhere." Who makes toothbrushes? Not the storekeeper. Oh no, he purchases them from the toothbrush manufacturer, who in turn employs dental

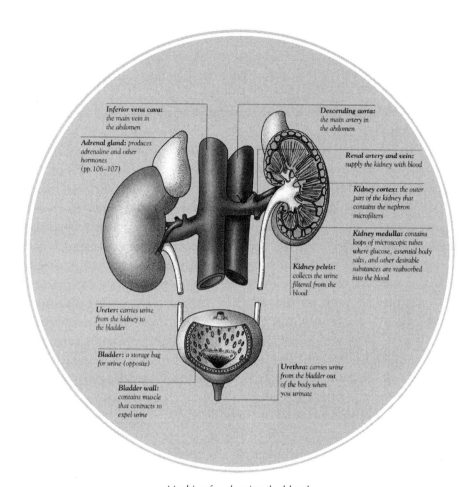

Machine for cleaning the blood

specialists and designers to produce a winning combination of effective bristle shape, ergonomic awareness (a handle that's easy to handle), and attractive color, at the lowest price possible. Every single toothbrush that has ever been manufactured carries the name of the company that produced it. They want you to recognize the name, so that the next toothbrush you purchase should be from the same company. Happy brushing !

Brushing one's teeth is a simple procedure, requiring such little skill (assuming you know the location of your mouth) that little children can perform the task admirably. Yet, everyone understands that the appropriate tool for the job, our toothbrush, needs to be specially designed, manufactured and sold. What would you say about a particularly difficult cleaning job, cleaning not a solid surface, but cleaning a liquid? What would you say about an appliance that cleans our blood?

Why should blood require cleaning? A car emits exhaust fumes. A heating furnace gives off smoke and soot. These are waste products. The body, with its numerous chemical reactions, likewise produces wastes. Most body wastes are end products of chemical reactions that are carried out in cells, as the cells build up new substances and break down old ones. (Living things are like vast, complex chemical factories. Hundreds of chemical changes and reactions occur every single second in each living cell. Bear in mind that the size of an individual cell is so small that several hundred of them could fit onto the period at the end of this sentence, that there are about 100 million million cells in a human body; each and every one is producing waste, and that waste has to be collected and eliminated; and you begin to realize the enormity of the task.) Examples of waste include urea, containing broken-down proteins, and creatinine, produced when muscles contract. These wastes are collected by the blood, the body's main transport fluid. They then need to be filtered. And that is no easy task.

Just consider the job at hand. Ail the blood in a person's body has to be filtered many times each day. The filtering process must not permit red blood cells or large particles of essential blood proteins to pass through, otherwise they might be lost to the body with rapid and calamitous results. In fact, 90 percent of the fluid that passes through the filters has to be reabsorbed. Essential vitamins, amino acids, glucose and hormones must be returned to the bloodstream. Imagine you eat a large portion of kippered herring, or any particularly salty food. If the high salt content was not removed by the filtering system, there might be real danger. Salt holds water. If it were permitted to remain in the blood, excess fluid would start accumulating in the blood, and in the spaces between the cells. The consequences of this could be dire. Potassium is another chemical substance that needs the most stringent control. It is obtained mainly from meat and fruit juices. If there is too little potassium, muscles begin to fail, particularly breathing muscles. A pinch too much acts as a brake on the heart. What type of machine can cope with such a variety of tasks?

The kidneys. The kidneys are two of the body's most remarkable organs. Just 4.5 inches long (that's smaller than a toothbrush), weighing 6 ounces, the kidney is the master chemist of the human body. The two kidneys sit on either side of the backbone, protected by the lower ribs. The diminutive maestro receives a plentiful blood supply, about 17.5 gallons every hour. This means that the body's blood passes through them 400 times each day. The blood enters the kidneys through the wide renal artery, and very slightly less goes back along the renal vein. This slight decrease in volume means that the kidneys are performing their vital cleansing job. The kidney's chief task is to filter the blood through microscopic filtering units called *nephrons*, and collect the wastes and unwanted substances from it to form *urine*. A single filtering unit in the kidneys would be sufficient reason to dance with joy. In fact, each single kidney contains approximately one million separate nephrons.

Every nephron is a wonder. Housed in the outer part of the kidneys, the microfilters receive blood. Because of the high pressure in the tiny capillaries that carry the blood (caused by the tortuous path through the capillaries that offers a resistance to the flow of blood), fluid is forced to filter out through the capillary walls, and is collected in an area called the *bowman's capsule.* Microscopic droplets of this waste-laden fluid pass out of each of the million nephrons and feed into a tiny reservoir at the center of the kidney. This in turn connects with the bladder, and the bladder with the outside. (You might be interested to know that the bladder is made of a special type of tissue that is strong and stretchable, and is resistant to the corrosive chemical nature of urine.) Wavelike muscular action occurs every 10-30 seconds, pushing the fluid along the exit tubes. At night, the activity slows down to a third of the daytime levels, permitting undisturbed sleep.

If all the substances that were filtered by the million nephrons would pass out as urine, the body would be sadly depleted. The reason that it doesn't happen is due to the remarkable workings of the kidneys. A series of various-sized pores in the nephron microfilters retain selected chemicals — according to the size, shape, and other features of their molecules, and allow other chemicals through. Red blood cells are large, and do not pass into the filtering system. All amino acids, glucose, and much of the water and some of the salts are reabsorbed into a network of capillaries surrounding the tubes. This selective reabsorption prevents the loss of useful substances from the blood, and regulates its composition. The remaining liquid is now called urine, and contains only the waste products that the body does not need.

The kidneys are incredibly efficient. Every minute, about 0.24 pints of water and chemicals pass from the blood into the tiny tubes. Yet so much water and useful substances are taken back from the tubes into the blood that only 0.002 pints of this is left as urine.

Certain things can increase the kidney's activity. When you are cold, for example, the blood supply to the skin is reduced — to preserve internal heat. (That is why when people are cold, they look pale.) This means an increased flow of blood to internal organs — including the kidneys. The more blood that flows through, the more urine is collected. In times of heat, the system is reversed. The small blood vessels in your skin become wider, so that more blood flows near the surface and gives off its extra heat to the air. You look flushed. Less blood to the internal organs, and the kidneys, and less urine is gathered. In times of anger, blood pressure rises, and the kidneys receive an extra supply of blood for processing. Result — increased urine output. This is another good reason to remain calm.

Alcohol has the opposite effect. On the underside of the brain lies the *pituitary gland.* This produces a hormone (chemical messenger) that controls the kidney's activity. Left to itself, the kidney might produce excess urine, resulting in dehydration. The hormone prevents this. Alcohol does not affect the kidneys directly, but it does dull the brain, retarding the production of the braking hormone. The kidneys, with the brakes removed, go into high gear, producing urine more rapidly. Caffeine in coffee has precisely the same effect.

The twin master-chemists, the two kidneys, silently and efficiently perform their vital tasks. Not for nothing does the *berachah* recited after emptying one's bladder speak about "many openings and cavities." Untangled and stretched out, the tubules in each kidney extend to some 70 miles of wondrous construction, complex and superefficient design, cleaning the blood and keeping the body healthy! The *berachah* is more than justified.

Everyone can see that a toothbrush is designed, the result of intelligent manufacture. Are the kidneys simpler, or more complicated? You don't have to be too wise to recognize wisdom. You just have to be honest.

Every family has one. They come in different sizes, sometimes very small, other times quite large; male or female, there is bound to be one. They are instantly recognizable. When the table is set for a meal, they will not immediately sit down. Instead, they surreptitiously creep over to the stove, and begin lifting lids. They need to know what's cooking, for they are fussy eaters. These are the people who instinctively sniff the food before putting it to their mouths (a habit picked up in yeshivah), and if the food is not to their liking, which is often, they will push away their plate, claiming,

"I'm not really hungry." These "not really hungry" folks will then sidle over to the pantry closet and scour the contents for some delectable dish (preferably with a chocolate covering) to assuage their pangs of hunger. Fussy eaters are always hungry, are allergic to yesterday's milk, the endpieces of bread, the lowest inch of the packet of breakfast cereal ("It's all powdery and horrible!"), tomatoes less than rock hard, or any apple with even the slightest hint of a bruise ("It's going moldy!"). You will find them at weddings calling back the waiter to ask if they can have a piece of dark chicken rather than the white meat that the poor chap inadvertently placed on their plate, and then when the waiter places the platter in front of them, they fuss and procrastinate while making the major decision of which piece will best suit their delicate palate.

One fussy eater per family is hard enough for the mother. Imagine now that you are cooking for an institution of several hundred hungry individuals, each of whom is fussy beyond description. Life would be tough indeed! Too much salt ... not enough paprika ... don't put mustard in the mayonnaise ... the *cholent* is too watery ... make sure that you put potatoes in the *cholent* ... potatoes in the *cholent* ruin the taste ... you put lemon juice in the green beans? ... the list is endless. There are some places (hotels and some hospitals) where the patrons are allowed to express their personal choice, and the management dutifully caters for them all. It is enormously difficult, extremely complicated, mistakes will always happen ("... but I told you specifically that I like my toast underdone ...") and the task can make life a nightmare for the personnel involved. Imagine now that you are the cook of an institution that has not several hundred members, not even several thousand, but a number so great that the only way that you can comprehend it is to say that for each person living in the world, there are 17,000. Are you serious? Which institution has approximately 60 *trillion* members?

The answer is your very own body, for that is the number of individual cells that you possess (give or take a few million). Every single cell requires nourishment to allow it to function, but the shopping list of individual tissue and organ cells are by no means identical. Some require protein; others fats; nerve cells need potassium; bone cells require calcium and fluorine; oxygen-carrying cells need iron, copper and manganese; whereas thyroid cells need iodine. Some cells are looking for vitamins, others for hormones, while still others are desperate for enzymes. One cell will want a microscope trace of cobalt, others will call for glucose, amino acids or a simple drink of water. Every cell needs something, and that something is as varied as chalk is from cheese. When you exercise, tissue requirements for just about everything increase enormously. How is this vast distribution system organized, where are the millions and millions of meals prepared, who delivers them to their correct destination, and how does each cell know what belongs specifically to it and to no other?

When you think of the transport system in the body, you have to think big. It is well known that within every human there runs a transport system with more than 60,000 miles of route — more than a global airline. An intricate arrangement of pumping (from the heart via the arteries) and muscular activity (squeezing the veins and pushing the blood upward, complete with regularly spaced valves to prevent backflow) guarantee a steady stream of life-giving blood that extends to the very extremities of the network. Volume and pressure are always kept at the same safe level. Efficient is not the word. Fresh supplies of oxygen and food are brought in as fast as they are consumed, and poisonous end products are never allowed to accumulate. Never think of the blood supply as a sluggish river, meandering along the highways and byways of the main-route arteries and little-lane capillaries — nothing could be further from the truth. The intricate pipeline system is so efficient that on average, a red cell will complete the circuit of the body in just 45 seconds. Just think of it — in slightly over a minute, the complete contents of the 60,000 mile-network which reaches every cell in the body, from ear lobe to little toe, will have circulated, not once but twice!

Thousands of cars – each one with its own destination

No journey could be as eventful as that experienced by a blood cell during its momentous odyssey. Take a tiny red blood cell (a single drop of blood contains millions of them). It has been charged with the task of carrying oxygen from the lungs to the tissues, and on the return journey, to carry carbon dioxide from the tissues to the lungs. This little cell has a very distinctive shape, looking like a disc which has been pressed in on either side, like the wheel of a car. This interesting shape has been specifically designed to give it a large surface area, so it can absorb more oxygen. It has a most peculiar feature in that it possesses no nucleus. Instead, the inside is filled with a red pigment called *hemoglobin*, and it is this that gives blood its familiar red color. Hemoglobin is a remarkable substance, and it is responsible for carrying the oxygen. When red blood cells pass through the lungs, the hemoglobin readily combines with oxygen, forming a complex compound. In this form, the red blood cell rushes to the tissues where another complicated chemical reaction occurs allowing it to release its oxygen, while at the same time collect the waste carbon dioxide. One of the vital ingredients of hemoglobin is iron, the reason why iron is so important to our diet. (The gas to keep away from is carbon monoxide. This gas is given off by burning fuel. It combines with hemoglobin about 300 times more readily than oxygen does with the result that if you inhale it, it displaces the oxygen from the red blood cells; and a lack of oxygen in the tissues is fatal. Carbon monoxide is present in coal gas, and also in car exhaust fumes. Small amounts of it are also present in cigarette smoke, which is why people who are not used to smoking feel faint when they smoke. Another good reason for giving up the obnoxious — in this case noxious — habit.)

Have you ever heard of mail trains that are equipped with a special hook to grab bags of mail from specially constructed structures as the train races through a station? That is similar to the situation of the red blood cell which passes through the lungs, and in a fraction of a second has to divest itself of the waste carbon dioxide while simultaneously picking up the vital oxygen package. To make it yet more wonderful, the process of the exchange is not mechanical, which would be remarkable enough, but chemical. Life itself depends on a complex chemical reaction which has to take place in the time that it takes you to blink. It works, countless times each day in millions of cells. Accidental?

Every time you eat, the food passes along to the central reservoir, called the stomach, and along the digestive system to the intestines. The food's important ingredients then pass in solution into the blood supply, where they are transferred to the liver. The liver is the body's amazing kitchen/chemical factory, and it is in the liver that many of the chemical reactions and manufacturing processes take place. (At any one time there can be more than 500 different chemical reactions taking place in the liver!) Indeed, like the chemical factory that it is, the liver then passes its finished products into the express transport system — the bloodstream. Think of the bloodstream as a vast conglomeration of chemicals, vitamins, enzymes, and minerals, repair and clotting materials, all jumbled together in a red whirlpool. The meals for all the cells are floating merrily along at high speed. It will all be circulated from head to toe. It is the responsibility of each cell to extract from the bloodstream that which is rightfully theirs. How will they manage? Let us say that you are under stress. The adrenal glands, above the kidneys, produce the hormone adrenalin, which needs to go immediately to your heart to tell it to beat faster. How will your heart know that it has to extract this vital hormone from the bloodstream that floods through it? When you swallow a pill to cure a headache, how does the brain know that it has to pick up the substance dissolved into the bloodstream, and not your big toe?

The answer is the greatest wonder of all. Each substance will only be accepted by the organ or the cell for which it is intended. In the same way that a specific key will only fit the lock for which it was designed to open, so the substance, although it will circulate through the whole body, will only be accepted by the organ or cell for which it is intended. Each cell has a sophisticated recognition system which will admit only the desired substance and refuse all others. Time allowed for acceptance or rejection — a split second.

Nothing could be more complex yet more vital to our very survival. It makes the job of the cook for the large institution seem quite tame in comparison, yet it helps us appreciate the breathtaking wisdom of the Greatest Organizer of all.

Note: Page numbers refer to the first time an entry is mentioned in a chapter.

This volume is part of
THE ARTSCROLL SERIES®
an ongoing project of
translations, commentaries and expositions
on Scripture, Mishnah, Talmud, Halachah,
liturgy, history, the classic Rabbinic writings,
biographies and thought.

For a brochure of current publications
visit your local Hebrew bookseller
or contact the publisher:

Mesorah Publications, ltd

4401 Second Avenue
Brooklyn, New York 11232
(718) 921-9000